Food Safety (General Food Hygiene) Regulations 1995

Food Safety (Temperature Control) Regulations 1995

Industry Guide to Good Hygiene Practice:

Catering Guide

Chadwick House
Group Ltd.

ISBN 0 900 103 00 0

PUBLISHED BY CHADWICK HOUSE GROUP LTD.

Chadwick Court
15 Hatfields
London SE1 8DJ

Tel: 0171 827 5882 Main switchboard: 0171 827 9929 Fax: 0171 827 9930
Chadwick House Group Ltd. (CHGL) is a commercial company, wholly owned by the Chartered Institute of Environmental Health (CIEH). The company's mission is to provide quality products and services to create awareness and to raise standards in the health environment and safety of the public. We intend to remain the premier provider by continual investment in our people, products and services in support of the aims of the CIEH. Our main activities are focused on training, communications and conferences and exhibitions. It also markets a wide selection of books and videos relating to environmental health. The CIEH is a professional and educational body, founded in 1883 and dedicated to the promotion of environmental health and to encouraging the highest possible standards in the training and the work of environmental health officers. The Chartered Institute has over 9,000 members most of whom work for local authorities in England, Wales and Northern Ireland. Apart from providing services and information to members, the Institute also advises government departments on environmental health and is consulted by them on any proposed legislation relevant to the work of environmental health officers.
The Chartered Institute is a Registered Charity.

Preface

This Industry Guide to good hygiene practice gives advice to catering businesses on how to comply with the Food Safety (General Food Hygiene) Regulations 1995. This is an official guide to the Regulations which has been developed in accordance with article 5 of the EC Directive on the hygiene of foodstuffs (93/43/EEC).

This guide also contains advice on how to comply with the Food Safety (Temperature Control) Regulations 1995.

Whilst this guide has no legal force, food authorities must give it due consideration when they enforce the Regulations. It is hoped that the information which this guide contains will help you both to meet your legal obligations and to ensure food safety.

Note: The Industry Guide to Good Hygiene Practice : Catering Guide was originally published in September 1995. This revised edition gives guidance on the Food Safety (General Food Hygiene) Regulations 1995 and now includes guidance on the Food Safety (Temperature Control) Regulations 1995. The guidance on the Food Safety (General Food Hygiene) Regulations has not been altered.

The guidance on the Food Safety (Temperature Control) Regulations can also be purchased separately, from the publishers of this Guide, Chadwick House Group Ltd.

Acknowledgements

The JHIC is indebted to the members of the Food Safety and Hygiene Working Group who developed this guide:

Representing BLRA

Tom Miller (Chairman of the working group) – Whitbread plc
Carolyn Smethurst – Allied Domecq Leisure

Representing BHA

David Clarke – Forte Purchasing
Nicki Rees – Compass Services (UK) Ltd
Clive Wadey – Compass Retail Catering

Representing Dept. of Health

John Barnes

Representing HCIMA

Robin Osner – Robin Osner Associates
Jennie Stokell – Jennie Stokell Catering Management

Representing LACOTS

Mark du Val

Representing RAGB

David Harrold

Secretary to the JHIC

Phil Phillips

The JHIC is grateful to all those members of its Associations who read the drafts and commented during the development process. In addition, all the valuable contributions received during the public consultation exercise were much appreciated.

Finally, thanks must go to Catherine MacDonald and Michelle Haylock for their software and keyboard skills.

Contents

Part 1   Introduction

Guide to Compliance by Caterers

This booklet is a guide for caterers on compliance with the Food Safety (General Food Hygiene) Regulations 1995 [FS(GFH)R 1995], the Food Safety (Temperature Control) Regulations 1995 [FS(TC)R 1995] and the equivalent regulations in Northern Ireland. It has been developed in accordance with Article 5 of the Directive 93/43/EEC and the preparation of this guide followed the 'Template' from the Department of Health (September 1994). The guide has the status implied by Reg. 8(2)(c) of FS(GFH)R 1995. Enforcement officers must give 'due consideration' to the guide when assessing compliance.

The guide deals only with the FS(GFH)R 1995 and the FS(TC)R 1995. Many other Acts or Regulations will govern the sale of food by caterers, and some may have a bearing on general food hygiene issues. For example, water supply (Schedule 1, Chapter VII) must also comply with water bye-laws; hygienic practices must also be consistent with Health & Safety requirements; date marking of supplies is dictated by food labelling regulations; and so on. There is specific cross-reference to other legal provisions in some parts of the guide, but it was impractical for this cross referencing to be comprehensive.

SCOPE & ORGANISATIONS: Listed on page 2 are the types of catering operation covered by the guide, which was drafted by members of the Joint Hospitality Industry Congress (JHIC). A list of the organisations involved in the JHIC is given at the end of this part of the guide.

Throughout, 'FOOD' includes drink and 'CATERING' is taken to include any sale or supply of food or drink for human consumption, including alcoholic drinks or soft drinks.

COMPLIANCE: The guide provides detailed, point by point, information on the legal requirements as they would be interpreted in catering premises. The primary objective of this guide is to give **comprehensive** guidance on legal **compliance**.

This guide sets out recommended means by which caterers may comply with the Hygiene Regulations. It may, of course, be possible for a business to demonstrate to enforcers that it has achieved the objectives of the Regulations in other ways.

GOOD PRACTICE/FOOD QUALITY: The guide gives additional information about points of good practice and factors that may affect food quality rather than safety. Although these points appear in the text, it is **NOT** a legal requirement to follow the advice on good practice and it is NOT intended to be comprehensive. Generally, advice is included only where there may be confusion about whether this point is a legal requirement or good practice (e.g. methods of hand drying). Many other Codes of Practice are available to give more detailed information on good practice. A publication of the IFST lists those codes of hygiene practice available in the UK (see references, Part 6).

PRACTICAL ADVICE ON TEMPERATURE CONTROL: An annex to Part 5 of the guide gives practical advice on temperature control of food. This does **not** form part of the guide to compliance with the Regulations to which food authorities must give due consideration.

DOCUMENTATION & RECORDS: There is NO explicit requirement anywhere in the regulations for caterers to document systems or to keep records. But in several areas, for example hygiene training, written records may be helpful to demonstrate compliance with the regulations. In addition, caterers faced with enforcement action under these regulations may be able to use the 'due diligence' defence of the Food Safety Act. Written down policies and records of routine checks may be very important in establishing the defence; this is especially true of records for the monitoring of critical control points (see Part 2).

• SCOPE

The Catering Sector covered by this guide includes the following types of operation:

- Banqueting
- Clubs
- Contract & In-House Catering (in the work place, institutions, schools, healthcare establishments, prisons, etc.)
- Delivered Catering and 'Meals on Wheels'
- Fish & Chip Restaurants
- *Food on the Move* (Trains, Coaches, Boats*, Aeroplanes*)
- Hotels & Guest Houses
- Mobile Snack Vehicles, Market Stalls
- Outdoor & Event Catering
- Private Party Caterers (including catering operations conducted from domestic premises)
- Public Houses
- Restaurants & Cafes of all types
- Sandwich Bars
- Takeaway & Fast Food Restaurants

* UK Regulations do not apply to aeroplanes or ships outside UK jurisdiction, but this guide will apply to commercial catering operations on boats on rivers and other inland waterways.

Joint Hospitality Industry Congress (JHIC)

Affiliated organisations:

Association of Licenced Multiple Retailers

Brewers and Licenced Retailers Association

British Holiday and Home Parks Association

British Hospitality Association

British Institute of Innkeeping

British Self Catering Association

Council for Hospitality Management Education

European Caterers Association (Great Britain)

Hotel & Catering International Management Association

Hotel and Catering Training Company

Local Authority Caterers Association

Restaurateurs Association of Great Britain

The guide was produced by a working party which included observers from the Department of Health and the Local Authorities Co-ordinating Body on Food and Trading Standards (LACOTS)

Prior to publication the document was circulated for wide consultation in accordance with the Template.

Preparation steps critical to food safety – identification and control

Regulation 4(3): A proprietor of a food business shall identify any step in the activities of the food business which is critical to ensuring food safety and ensure that adequate safety procedures are identified, implemented, maintained and reviewed …

This regulation is a new legal requirement. It is different to anything in previous general Hygiene Regulations. It is designed to make businesses focus on the activities critical to food safety in their business, and to find ways of controlling them.

This section of the guide provides advice on this requirement. For reasons of space, the guide gives an outline of the legal requirement and what it means for caterers. Many other documents give more detailed guidance on this approach to food safety. In particular, guidance for caterers is given in 'Assured Safe Catering' and 'Systematic Assessment of Food Environment' ['S.A.F.E.']. Details of availability are given in Part 6. A few practical examples are given in this guide, more detailed examples will be found in these two booklets.

Every catering business is different. There will be a different menu, different equipment, different systems of drinks dispense, and different methods of food preparation and service. **Every caterer must apply the principles to their own business.**

This will involve looking at the operation step by step, from the selection of ingredients and suppliers through to service of food to the customer. There will be some steps at which hazards exist and steps at which they can be controlled. Many of the controls will be simple common sense practices that caterers have followed for years. The hazard analysis approach means the planning of food safety in easy logical steps. It should give a clearer focus on the controls that are important to an individual business to ensure safe food is provided.

The approach is based on five principles which are part of the legal requirement and which are covered in the following section.

Regulation	Guide to compliance
4(3)(a) analysis of the potential food hazards in a food business operation;	FOOD HAZARDS: A hazard is anything that could cause harm to the consumer. There are three main hazards that may arise with food served in catering premises. These are contamination of food by: ● Bacteria or other micro-organisms that cause food poisoning. ● Chemicals, for example by cleaning materials or pest baits. ● Foreign material such as glass, metal, plastic and so on. Of these, the most important hazard is likely to be harmful bacteria or other germs that may contaminate and grow in food. Every operation will have different hazards depending upon the range of foods sold and the methods of preparation. Every operator must identify the possible hazards in their own business.
4(3)(b) identification of the points in those operations where food hazards may occur;	Food passes through many steps; delivery, storage, preparation, cooking, cooling and so on. Hazards can occur at many or all of the steps. For each type of food, the hazards that may occur at each step should be identified. Mostly these will be steps in the operation where: ● food can become CONTAMINATED with micro-organisms, chemicals or foreign material. ● bacteria can GROW if the food is held too long at the wrong temperature. ● micro-organisms SURVIVE a process that should kill them. For example when cooking or disinfection of equipment is inadequate.
4(3)(c) deciding which of the points identified are critical to ensuring food safety ("critical points");	CRITICAL POINTS are steps at which the hazards must be controlled to ensure that a hazard is eliminated or reduced to a safe level. ● Any step where food may become CONTAMINATED should be controlled. Controls will include clean and disinfected equipment, the personal hygiene of staff, and separation of raw and cooked food. All food should be protected from contamination by foreign bodies, pests or chemicals. ● Steps where bacteria may be able to GROW in food must be controlled. The time and temperature at which food is held, stored or displayed are likely to be critical. ● Any cooking or reheating step should be able to KILL harmful micro-organisms. It will be critical that heating is thorough. Cooking is normally the most important control step in most food preparation. Chemical disinfection of equipment is another control point designed to KILL micro-organisms. There are some steps where hazards cannot or need not be controlled. For example, no matter how good your supplier, some raw chickens will contain Salmonella on delivery. There must be points later in the process [for example, cooking] that will control the hazard. Steps where hazards can be effectively controlled should be identified as critical control points.
4(3)(d) identification and implementation of effective control and monitoring procedures at those critical points; and	There are two points here. Controls must be set for the critical points, then checks introduced. CONTROLS will either reduce a hazard to an acceptable level or get rid of it completely. The controls should be as precise as possible. For example, it is better to state that raw meat will be stored under refrigeration at a set temperature, rather than to simply say that it must be kept in the chiller.

Regulation	Guide to compliance

A control target should be set for every critical control point that has been identified.

When controls have been set, it is then possible to MONITOR the critical points whenever that preparation step is used. The targets can be checked. The frequency of checks should be set for each control. It is not necessary to measure critical points every time a step is performed, it may be enough to do checks at intervals. In some cases it may be useful to keep records. For example, it may allow the manager or supervisor to check that the system is being followed. But it is not essential to keep records for each and every control.

Checking temperatures does not always involve probing food with a thermometer. Delivery vans or storage chillers may be fitted with temperature readouts, and these can be checked. (Air temperature measurements do not always reflect the temperature of food at every part of the chiller or van. Occasional cross checks should be made.) For cooking or cooling, you may have established that a certain combination of time and temperature in the oven gives an acceptable result. Batch by batch, it may be good enough just to check that the setting is correct and the batch is processed for the right time. Periodically there should be a cross check using a probe thermometer.

Other critical controls are more difficult to measure, for example cleaning & disinfection of equipment or the personal hygiene of staff. They will often be vital to the safety of food, and there should be regular checks that standards are kept up. This may simply be visual checks by the manager or supervisor. Cleaning schedules may play a part.

Some controls will be the same for many different foods, and this makes monitoring very much easier. It does not have to be done item by item. For example many perishable raw materials will be kept under refrigeration at 5°C or cooler. One check of the fridge temperature controls a large number of foods in that fridge.

Corrective action: If monitoring shows that control is not satisfactory, it is important to take corrective action. For example,
- poor cleaning of food contact equipment – take out of service and clean again
- poor fridge temperatures – adjust or repair
- inadequate cooking temperature – return to heat for further cooking

The chart at the end of this part of the guide gives an example of steps, hazards, controls and monitoring procedures that may apply to a typical catering operation. It is important to remember that each operation is different and the proprietor must focus on the actual hazards and controls that are critical to his operation.

4(3)(e) review of the analysis of food hazards, the critical control points and the control and monitoring procedures periodically, and whenever the food business's operations change.

It is NOT satisfactory simply to go through this process once and then forget about it. This part of the regulation says that it must be kept up to date. From time to time the system may need to be reviewed and amended, for example:

- If controls or methods of checking are found to be ineffective or impracticable.
- The menu changes. New dishes may have new hazards and controls.
- The method of preparation changes. For example, a change from commercially prepared mayonnaise to 'home made' will introduce a number of new critical points that will need to be controlled.
- New equipment is introduced. For example, the time and temperature that gave adequate cooking in one oven may not be the same in a different model.

Examples of Generalised Analysis of Critical Steps, Hazards, Controls and Monitoring

Step	Hazard	Control*	Monitoring
Purchase & Delivery	Instrinsic contaminant (Micro-organisms or Foreign Material)	Use reputable suppliers	Check delivery vehicles Check date codes, temperatures and condition of food
Storage	Bacterial Growth Further Contamination (by Micro-organisms, Foreign Material or Chemicals)	Store at correct temperatures Cover/wrap foods Separate raw/cooked, high risk foods Stock rotation	Check temperatures Visual checks Check date marks
Preparation	Bacterial Growth Further Contamination	Limit time at kitchen temperatures Use clean equipment Good personal hygiene	Visual checks Cleaning Schedules
Cooking	Survival of Bacteria	Cook to centre temperature above 75°C	Check temperatures
Cooling	Growth of Surviving Spores Further Contamination	Cool food rapidly. (Set a time period appropriate to dish). Refrigerate when cooled – below 5°C. Keep foods covered, where possible.	Check time and temperature
Chilled Storage	Growth of Bacteria Further Contamination	Store at correct temperatures Cover/wrap foods/stock rotation Separate raw/cooked foods	Check temperatures Visual checks
Reheating	Survival of Bacteria	Reheat to centre temperature above 75°C (In Scotland 82°C is required for some foods)	Check temperatures
Hot Holding & Service	Growth of Bacteria Further Contamination	Keep food above 63°C Use clean equipment Keep covered, where possible	Check temperatures Visual checks
Cold Service	Growth of Bacteria Further Contamination	Keep cool or display for a maximum of 4 hours Use clean equipment Keep covered, where possible	Check temperature and time Visual checks

* Suggested controls in this chart are indicative of good practice and for some foods only. For example, some cuts of meat may have no significant contamination in the centre, and cooking to temperatures below 75°C (rare) is acceptable. They are not intended to be minimum compliance standards for all foods. Other foods or drinks may involve different handling or preparation steps. These will need to be analysed accordingly.

Establishing a system

The proprietor has the legal obligation to establish a system and keep it under review. It is often helpful to involve **key** staff in developing it and **all** staff need to know the part that they have to play in making it work.

A business may take a simple approach to the principles required in the regulation or may choose to do a much more detailed and thorough analysis. This may depend upon the size and nature of the business, and the expertise available.

Documentation

Hazard Analysis Critical Control Point (HACCP) systems used in food factories will often involve a great deal of documentation of the system, and will then generate many written records. **This regulation does NOT demand fully documented 'classic' HACCP**. But caterers should bear in mind that a brief written explanation of their system would be helpful to show the Environmental Health Officer (EHO) that this regulation has been complied with.

Equally, the regulation does NOT demand written records of **monitoring** [see 4(3)(d)]. But caterers should remember that, if action is taken under the Food Safety Act 1990, they may have a defence of 'due diligence'. Written records may be invaluable in establishing that defence.

In short, you do not have to have large quantities of paperwork, but some documentation will help.

Where to find more information

More detailed guidance for caterers on applying the principles is available in:

- *Assured Safe Catering (ASC), Department of Health, HMSO £8.50*

- *S.A.F.E. (Systematic Assessment of Food Environment), British Hospitality Association £5.50*

Both of these guides also contain a great deal of information, especially on food poisoning organisms, that will help caterers to understand the hazards that may occur.

Contact addresses are given in Part 6.

Part 3 Food hygiene supervision and instruction and/or training

This is a new legal requirement in Schedule 1 Chapter X [Regulation 4 (2) (d)]:

"The proprietor of a food business shall ensure that food handlers engaged in the food business are supervised and instructed and/or trained in food hygiene matters commensurate with their work activities".

Food Handler

The legal requirement applies only to a 'food handler'. For the purposes of this guide to the training requirement, **'Food Handler'** means:

Any person involved in a food business who handles or prepares food whether open (unwrapped) or packaged. [Food includes drink and ice].

Stages of Supervision & Instruction and/or Training

This section identifies three stages of supervision/instruction/training. Different stages will be needed for different food handlers. Three categories of food handlers (A, B & C) are described who *must* be supervised and instructed and/or trained. Other staff who are not food handlers may need some instruction or training as a matter of good practice.

The training needed will relate to the actual job of the individual. It will also relate to the type of food that they handle. Staff who handle 'high risk' food will need more training than those who handle 'low risk' foods. Special arrangements may have to be made for persons whose first language is not English and/or persons with learning or literacy difficulties.

The following guidance indicates how a proprietor may comply with this requirement and suggests additional points of good practice. But it would be possible for a food business to demonstrate to enforcers that it had achieved the objectives identified in the regulations in other ways.

Training of food handlers beyond the legal requirement may be carried out as a matter of good practice as their career develops and they take on extra responsibility.

SUPERVISION & INSTRUCTION: All staff should be properly supervised and instructed to ensure that they work hygienically. A greater degree of supervision may be needed:

- for new staff awaiting formal training;
- for staff handling high risk foods;
- for less experienced staff.

Even if staff have received formal training, supervision must depend upon the competence and experience of the individual food handler.

Where an operation employs only one or two people supervision may not be practical. In such cases, training must be sufficient to allow work to be unsupervised.

Job titles are given in the following paragraphs, but a given title can encompass wide variations of work activities in different situations. The standards indicated in this guide are summarised in the following table:

	Stage 1	Stage 2	Stage 3	
Category of Staff	'The Essentials of Food Hygiene'	Hygiene Awareness Instruction	Formal Training Level 1	Formal Training Level 2 and/or 3
Category A Handle low risk or wrapped food only	Guide to compliance [before starting work for the first time]	Guide to compliance [within 4 weeks; 8 week part-time staff]		
Category B Food handlers who prepare open, 'high risk' foods.	Guide to compliance [before starting work for the first time]	Guide to compliance [within 4 weeks]	Guide to compliance [within 3 months]	
Category C Food handlers who also have a supervisory role	Guide to compliance [before starting work for the first time]	Guide to compliance [within 4 weeks]	Guide to compliance [within 3 months]	Good practice [according to responsibilities]

This table is intended only as a summary. The detail of who must be trained and to what stage of training, and when, is given in the following pages.

Food Safety (General Food Hygiene) Regulations 1995 – Guide to compliance by Caterers

Other Staff

Other staff who are not food handlers may also need instruction, supervision or training as a matter of good practice.

This may include kitchen cleaners and any other support staff who visit the kitchen and also those who are involved in the operation such as, site engineers or maintenance fitters. They should understand the *Essentials of Food Hygiene* as part of their induction to the job, and should have appropriate elements of *Hygiene Awareness Instruction* within three months of starting.

More senior supervisors and managers who do not actually handle food, but who may have a direct influence on the hygienic operation of the business should also receive training as a matter of good practice. They should have training in food hygiene appropriate to their job and their level of responsibility. For many of these, training may include formal training (Stage 3) to at least Level 1, possibly progressing to Levels 2 or 3 as their career and responsibilities develop.

A wide range of job titles may be included, such as hotel manager, regional or area manager, food buyer, production manager, quality assurance manager, and so on.

Stage 1 – The essentials of food hygiene

Guide to compliance	Advice on good practice
All food handlers Before anyone is allowed to start work for the first time, a **food handler** must receive written or verbal instruction in the Essentials of Food Hygiene.	All other staff employed in the business should also receive similar instruction as a matter of good practice. Any visitors to the premises should also be instructed on those rules that relate to personal hygiene.

The essentials of food hygiene

- Keep yourself clean and wear clean clothing.
- Always wash your hands thoroughly: before handling food, after using the toilet, handling raw foods or waste, before starting work, after every break, after blowing your nose.
- Tell your supervisor, before commencing work, of any skin, nose, throat, stomach or bowel trouble or infected wound. You are breaking the law if you do not.
- Ensure cuts and sores are covered with a waterproof, high visibility dressing.
- Avoid unnecessary handling of food.
- Do not smoke, eat or drink in a food room, and never cough or sneeze over food.
- If you see something wrong – tell your supervisor.
- Do not prepare food too far in advance of service.
- Keep perishable food either refrigerated or piping hot.
- Keep the preparation of raw and cooked food strictly separate.
- When reheating food ensure it gets piping hot.
- Clean as you go. Keep all equipment and surfaces clean.
- Follow any food safety instructions either on food packaging or from your supervisor.

These points can be amended to suit each business. Some points may not be relevant to some businesses.

Stage 2 – Hygiene awareness instruction

All Food Handlers [Category A, B & C staff] must have this stage of training. This training will form a module of Stage 3 training.

Guide to compliance

Category A – Food handlers

Job:
On-site support and front-of-house activities *not* directly involving the preparation and personal handling of high risk open (unwrapped) food

Likely job title:
Storeman, waiter/waitress, bar staff (serving food and drink but not involved in food preparation), counter staff, servery assistant, cellarman, food delivery staff

Level:
Hygiene Awareness Instruction.

When:
Full-time staff: At induction or as soon as practical thereafter and ideally within 4 weeks of appointment.
Part-time and casual staff: Likewise but, with their shorter hours, within 8 weeks should be the target.

Hygiene awareness instruction

The following is an outline of HYGIENE AWARENESS INSTRUCTION. The overall aim is to develop a knowledge of the basic principles of food hygiene. The topics covered should be appropriate to the job of the individual, and may include:

- The business's policy – priority given to food hygiene
- "Germs" – potential to cause illness
- Personal health and hygiene – need for high standards, reporting illness, rules on smoking
- Cross contamination – causes, prevention
- Food storage – protection, temperature control
- Waste disposal, cleaning and disinfection – materials, methods and storage
- 'Foreign body' contamination
- Awareness of pests

In addition, staff must be told how to do their particular job hygienically. In particular, they should be instructed on any control or monitoring points from the 'Identification of Critical Steps' (Part 2 of this Guide).

The depth, breadth, and duration of the training will be dependent upon the particular job requirement and the degree of risk involved in the activity. It may be split into modules. The design of the sessions should be such that they encourage discussion and group involvement.

Food Safety (General Food Hygiene) Regulations 1995 – Guide to compliance by Caterers

Stage 3 – Formal training

Formal training at three levels is described on page 14. Category B & C staff must have formal training in food hygiene to level 1. For category C food handlers, it is good practice for training to progress to levels 2 or 3 as their career and responsibilities progress.

Guide to compliance	Advice on good practice
Category B Food handlers **Activity:** Preparation and handling of high risk open (unwrapped) foods. **Likely job title:** Commis chef, cook, catering supervisor, kitchen assistant & bar staff who prepare food. **Level:** At least to **Level 1*** **When:** Within 3 months of appointment, or as soon as possible afterwards. (Subject to training being available). Hygiene Awareness Instruction must be carried out in the interim and will form a module of Level 1.	**Category B – Food handlers**
Category C Food handlers **Activity:** Managers or supervisors who handle any type of food. **Likely job title:** Unit manager, unit supervisor, chef manager, bar or pub managers, chef, operations general manager. (That is, staff based on-site with a direct management role and handling food). Owner/operator of home catering or mobile catering business. **Level:** At least to **Level 1*** **When:** Within 3 months of appointment, or as soon as possible afterwards. (Subject to training being available). Hygiene Awareness Instruction must be carried out in the interim and will form a module of Level 1.	**Category C – Food handlers** It may be good practice for staff in these grades to take further training to **Level 2 or Level 3*** as their career and management responsibilities progress. The need will depend upon the actual nature of their duties. *** see following page for an indication of the different levels of training.**

Stage 3 Formal training courses

Three levels of formal Training have been mentioned previously in this Part

LEVEL 1

The following is an outline of Level 1 training. The overall aim is to develop a level of understanding of the basic principles of food hygiene.

- Food poisoning micro-organisms types and sources
- Simple microbiology, toxins, spores, growth & death
- Premises & equipment
- Common food hazards – physical, chemical, microbiological
- Personal Hygiene – basic rules and responsibilities
- Preventing food contamination
- Food poisoning, symptoms and causes
- Cleaning & disinfection
- Legal obligations
- Pest control
- Effective temperature control of food e.g. storage, thawing, reheating, and cooking

Such a course will probably be of about 6 hours duration.

In some larger organisations in-house training may be used to deliver this level. In-house food hygiene training *of appropriate standard* will satisfy the legal requirement even if they are not formally accredited by one of the organisations mentioned below.

Alternatively, a range of standard food hygiene courses are accredited and run by several organisations. These include:

- The Chartered Institute of Environmental Health (CIEH)
- The Royal Institute of Public Health and Hygiene (RIPHH)
- The Royal Society of Health (RSH)
- The Royal Environmental Health Institute of Scotland (REHIS)
- Society of Food Hygiene Technology (SOFHT)

LEVELS 2 & 3

More advanced training (Level 2 & 3) courses will deal with food hygiene in more detail and cover management and systems. Again this training may be delivered 'in-house'. Alternatively a variety of courses are offered by the organisations mentioned above. Typically, **Level 2** will involve courses of 12 to 24 hours duration and **Level 3** will involve courses of 24 to 40 hours duration.

Trainers

As a matter of good practice trainers themselves should be adequately trained. Trainers of Level 1 courses should be trained in food hygiene to Level 1 or above. In addition, they *should* be trained in training skills or able to demonstrate competence. Trainers of higher level courses *should* have appropriately higher levels of knowledge.

Test/Assessment

After formal training it is good practice that food handlers should be assessed to test their understanding of the principles. Assessment may be a multiple choice test paper or a verbal test.

VOCATIONAL COURSES – food hygiene training does NOT have to be conducted as a separate exercise. Many vocational courses will include food hygiene training. Food handlers do not have to take additional hygiene training if their vocational training (e.g. NVQ/SVQ) has provided hygiene training to the appropriate level. Special arrangements may have to be made for problems of literacy or foreign language.

General Points

Existing Staff

Staff already employed before the introduction of the 1995 Regulations should be instructed or trained as soon as is practical to the level indicated according to their job.

New Employees

All new employees *must* be told how to do their specific job hygienically. New employees may claim that they have already been trained. If they cannot provide documentation to support this, the employer should assume that they have NOT been trained.

Agency Staff

Agency staff may be employed in most of the staff categories identified above. The proprietor of the catering business must:

- Instruct all staff in the 'Essentials of Food Hygiene'.
- Satisfy himself that staff whose work needs higher stages of training have been trained accordingly.
- If they cannot provide documentation, then the proprietor should assume that they are not trained and deploy or supervise them accordingly.

It is good practice for **employment agencies** to:

- Train staff who they employ regularly to the stage appropriate to the job that they would normally do.
- Provide documentary evidence to the hirer.

Training Plan & Records

It is good practice for a business to have a training plan to identify the training needed for each member of staff.

In addition, it is good practice to keep records of the training completed by every member of staff. **Records are not needed to comply with the law.** However, written evidence of hygiene training may be very important in demonstrating compliance with the requirement. Records may also be relevant when attempting to establish a 'due diligence' defence.

Training needs should be reviewed on a regular basis. Refresher or update training may be necessary at intervals. The frequency should be related to the risk and nature of the business and the food handled, also the skill, competence and experience of the individual employee. The key points of hygiene principles can be reinforced. In addition, this training can take account of any changes in the business, for example changes in menu or production systems may raise new hygiene issues and controls. Any faults that have been identified can also be addressed.

Part 4   The 'Rules of hygiene'

The following is a guide to Schedule 1 of the Regulations.

Column 1
quotes the provisions of the Schedule.

Column 2
provides the interpretation of the provision, for example steps that can be taken to comply with the point in the schedule. Note that points in the actual regulation are not always repeated in column 2. Column 2 must be read in conjunction with column 1.

Column 3
This column provides additional information on good catering practice. It is NOT part of the legal requirement for compliance with the regulations.

Good practice may include points that reinforce the legal requirement, for example indications of how the legal requirement may be achieved.

Good practice also includes points that may impact on food quality rather than Food Safety. Where this is the case, it is indicated in the text.

Guidance on Good/Best Practice or on food quality issues is not meant to be comprehensive. There are many other excellent guides to good practice. Many of these deal with particular types of operation within the very wide 'catering' sector.

Note that Chapters 1 & 2 of the Schedule should be read together. General points on structure and layout are made in Chapter 1 (which applies to the entire premises). Many of these are defined more specifically (in relation to food rooms) in Chapter 2.

Part 4 The 'Rules of hygiene'

Chapter I General requirements for food premises

Food premises are any premises or areas of premises in which food or drink is prepared, served or stored. This Chapter applies to the kitchen and all ancillary areas of the premises, storage areas, cellars, toilets, staff rooms, etc.

Legal requirement

1 Food premises must be kept clean and maintained in good repair and condition

Guide to compliance

- The internal surfaces of the structure and equipment fixed to the structure, including light fittings, ventilation and any other equipment must be visually clean and in a good state of repair.

- Food premises must be maintained to a standard that will allow effective cleaning.

Ultimately, standards must be appropriate to the type of catering business, the type of food that is handled and how it is presented and prepared.

More specific information is given in Chapter II on structural materials for rooms where food is prepared treated or processed and for food contact surfaces.

Some parts of the premises such as cellars and store rooms will not be covered by Chapter II. These will be areas in which open food is not prepared, treated or processed. Wall, floor and ceiling finishes will be acceptable in these areas that would not be acceptable in food preparation areas. Such finishes as bare blocks or brick walls will be suitable in some parts of the premises.

Advice on good practice

It is good practice to 'clean as you go' but food contact surfaces should always be cleaned at the end of every shift.

Non food contact surfaces and those that are not subject to a significant risk of contamination e.g. high wall surfaces, extract ventilation, should receive periodic cleaning. The frequency should relate to the build up of dirt.

Good practice requires systematic cleaning schedules for all surfaces and equipment.

There should be a separate cleaning schedule for every piece of equipment and every area of the premises.

A cleaning schedule should identify:
- the task to be done
- frequency
- cleaning material and chemicals to be used
- the method (including details of strip down and reassembly of the equipment)
- safety precautions
- who does the job
- standard expected

Effective application of cleaning schedules should be monitored by the manager or supervisor.

---

2 The layout, design, construction and size of food premises shall:
(a) permit adequate cleaning and/or disinfection

The criterion is cleanability. Layout and design should allow access for effective cleaning.

Alternatively equipment must be mobile to enable adequate cleaning and disinfection.

The amount and type of cleaning needed will relate to the area of the premises and the use to which it is put.

Materials of construction must be suitable to allow the type of cleaning appropriate to that area. More information is given in Chapter II.

Legal requirement	Guide to compliance	Advice on good practice
(b) be such as to protect against the accumulation of dirt,	The layout, design, construction and size of premises must avoid the accumulation of dirt in places inaccessible to cleaning.	It is good practice to avoid sharp corners at wall or floor junctions by coving.
contact with toxic materials,	Construction materials must not include any substance that may add toxic material to food either by direct contact or vapour.	
the shedding of particles into food	Design and construction, especially of high level surfaces, should avoid finishes that may lead to shedding of particles such as flaking paint, plaster or fibres.	
and the formation of condensation or undesirable mould on surfaces.	Any growth of mould within the fabric of the building is undesirable.	
	Design, construction, layout, and size of the premises must be planned to avoid the build-up of condensation. Special attention must be given to areas where steam and humidity are generated.	
	This will be linked to the type of ventilation system installed.	
(c) permit good food hygiene practices, including protection against cross-contamination between and during operations, by foodstuffs,	There must be enough space in storage and food preparation rooms to allow high risk food to be prepared on separate work surfaces and equipment, if they have to be handled in the same area at the same time as food that may contaminate them.	Good layout, operating systems and production flow should ensure that preparation and handling of high risk foods are segregated.
	(If handling low and high risk foods happen at different times, the same area may be used provided it is able to be properly cleaned and disinfected between operations.)	In addition to proofing possible entry points, it is good practice to have secondary defences against pests which may include pest baits (which should be laid by competent contractors) and electronic fly killers. Electronic fly killers should not be located over work surfaces.
equipment,	Equipment requirements are given in more detail in Chapter V.	It is good practice that premises should be designed so that refuse does not have to be taken through food rooms for collection.
materials,	Materials must be cleanable according to their intended use.	
water,	Water used for food production purposes (including ice and steam) must not contaminate the food. More detail is given in Chapter VII. Care should be taken to prevent unintended cross-contamination by, for example, rain water leaking into storage areas.	
air supply	Air supply must be designed so that contaminated air is not brought into food rooms. More detail is given under provisions 5 & 6 of this Chapter and Chapter II (1)(d).	

Legal requirement	Guide to compliance	Advice on good practice
or personnel and	Facilities must be provided for good personal hygiene. More detail is given under provisions 3 and 9 of this Chapter; in Chapter III (2) and in Chapter VIII.	
external sources of contamination such as pests.	Premises must be designed to prevent pest access and harbourage. More detail is given under other provisions notably Chapter II (1) (d), Chapter VI (3) and Chapter IX (3). Separate storage of cleaning materials is detailed in Chapter IX (4).	
(d) provide, where necessary, suitable temperature conditions for the hygienic processing and storage of products.	Design and construction of food preparation rooms should avoid the build up of excessive temperatures. Food storage rooms must be capable of keeping food at suitable temperatures. Some foods are subject to specific temperature controls.	
3 An adequate number of washbasins must be available,	The number of washbasins will depend on the size of the business and the size and layout of the premises.	
suitably located and designated for cleaning hands.	Wash basins must be located close to toilet facilities and at strategic places in the premises so that any worker has convenient access to them. Wash basins must be used for hand washing only.	It is good catering practice to site wash basins by the entrance to kitchens. In larger premises extra wash basins may be needed especially where 'high risk' foods are handled.
An adequate number of flush lavatories must be available and connected to an effective drainage system.	Toilets must be provided on the basis of the Workplace (Health, Safety and Welfare) Regulations 1992. The minimum requirement is 1 toilet or WC for up to 5 employees. [Note: Applies to premises built or converted since Jan 1 1993. ALL other premises must comply by Jan 1 1996] Toilets must be connected to a drainage system through an effective trap.	There should be an intervening ventilated space between toilets and food rooms. Food should not be stored in that space. It is good practice to have toilet facilities for catering staff separate from those for guests and other visitors.
Lavatories must not lead directly into rooms in which food is handled.	Toilets (either WC or urinals) must not open directly into a food room. NOTE: For outdoor events, mobiles, and domestic premises used for commercial food preparation, different standards may apply. See Chapter III.	

Legal requirement	Guide to compliance	Advice on good practice
4 *Washbasins for cleaning hands must be provided with hot and cold (or appropriately mixed) running water,*	A single mixer tap is acceptable, or water supplied from an instant heating unit.	It is good practice to supply warm water for hand washing at about 45°C through a single tap which is preferably not operated by hand.
materials for cleaning hands	A supply of soap or detergent must be provided for cleaning hands.	It is good practice to use bactericidal detergent from a dispenser. Antiseptic rubs (applied to clean hands) provide an alternative to bactericidal soap.
and for hygienic drying.	Drying facilities may include: ● disposable paper ● roller paper cabinet towels ● washable fabric 'roller towels' in cabinets ● warm air dryers	Any towel on which the same part can be used more than once is not recommended. Air dryers can be provided but tend not to be used efficiently.
Where necessary, the provision for washing food must be separate from the hand washing facility.	In all premises there must be a separate basin that is only used for hand washing. NOTE: Different provisions for mobile or temporary premises are given in Chapter III.	It is good practice to have signs to identify designated 'HAND WASH' basins. Where nail brushes are provided they must be kept clean.
5 *There must be suitable and sufficient means of natural or mechanical ventilation.*	Natural or mechanical ventilation must be provided to ensure that heat and/or humidity do not build up to levels that could compromise the safety of food.	As a target, ambient temperatures should be below 25°C. Natural ventilation in rooms where food is cooked will only be suitable in small premises and where there is low heat input to the room.
Mechanical air flow from a contaminated area to a clean area must be avoided.	Air mechanically drawn into 'clean' preparation rooms, producing ready to eat food must not be drawn from dirty areas such as waste storage areas or rooms used for 'dirty' processes such as pot wash.	
Ventilation systems must be so constructed as to enable filters and other parts requiring cleaning or replacement to be readily accessible.	Filters and other parts of the system must be accessible either directly or through access panels.	
6 *All sanitary conveniences within food premises shall be provided with adequate natural or mechanical ventilation.*	Toilets must have either natural or mechanical ventilation to prevent (as far as possible) aerosols and offensive odours from permeating food rooms.	Mechanical systems should discharge away from food rooms.
7 *Food premises must have adequate natural and/or artificial lighting.*	Lighting must be good enough to allow safe food handling, effective cleaning and the monitoring of cleaning standards.	Recommended illumination levels range from 150 lux in store rooms to 500 lux in food preparation areas. Glass lights should be protected with shatterproof diffusers or shrouds in areas where open food is handled.

Legal requirement	Guide to compliance	Advice on good practice
8 Drainage facilities must be adequate for the purpose intended; they must be designed and constructed to avoid the risk of contamination of foodstuffs.	Drains must have sufficient fall to allow all solid and liquid waste to flow away. All appliances connected to the drainage system must be provided with an effective trap. Inspection points must be available, but they must be adequately sealed.	The direction of the flow should be away from 'clean' areas to 'dirty' areas. Toilets should feed into the system after the kitchen, and there should be adequate traps. If open floor drains are provided, grids should be easy to clean.
9 Adequate changing facilities for personnel must be provided where necessary.	Provision must be made to allow handlers to change and to store their street clothes and personal effects away from open foods. Depending upon the size of the operation and numbers of employees, a changing area away from foods and lockable secure cupboards may be adequate to meet this requirement.	Where staff wear protective clothing, it is good practice to have separate changing rooms and to provide secure storage for personal effects.

Part 4 The 'Rules of hygiene'

Chapter II Specific requirements for rooms where foodstuffs are prepared, treated or processed (excluding dining areas and those premises specified in Chapter III)

SCOPE Note that this Chapter applies ONLY to rooms in which food or drink are prepared, treated or processed. It does NOT apply to food storage rooms or other ancillary areas within the food premises such as cellars.

DINING AREAS The requirements of this chapter do NOT apply to Dining Areas, that is areas in which ready to eat food is served to the person who will consume it. Service of food may be self-service or waiter/waitress service.

In catering outlets, it is common to find layouts in which FOOD PREPARATION areas and DINING areas are continuous parts of the same room. There will often be a clear demarcation, usually a counter, between the two.

The DINING AREA is the area where food and drink is consumed. A similar demarcation is common in Bars.

The areas and equipment in these rooms where food is prepared will be subject to the requirements of this chapter.

If a restaurant engages in some food preparation at the tables in the Dining Area, for example flambé, this does not mean that the dining area must comply with these structural requirements.

Legal requirement	Guide to compliance	Advice on good practice
1 *In rooms where food is prepared, treated or processed (excluding dining areas):* *(a) floor surfaces must be maintained in a sound condition and they must be easy to clean and, where necessary, disinfect.* *This will require the use of impervious, non absorbent, washable and non-toxic materials, unless the proprietor of the food business can satisfy the food authority that other materials used are appropriate.*	Floors must be kept in a good state of repair that allows them to be kept clean. Disinfection will reduce contamination in the kitchen environment. Frequent disinfection of floors in catering establishments is not essential provided floors are kept clean. Exceptions would be the 'high risk' areas of cook chill units where bacterial contamination from the environment may have the chance to develop to unsafe levels over the storage life of the product. Assuming that they are properly installed, floor surfaces that would comply with this requirement include: Flooring tiles (quarry, ceramic or vinyl), Vinyl safety flooring, Terrazzo, Cast in situ resin flooring.	It is good practice to disinfect all floors periodically. The frequency will depend upon the nature of the activity.
Where appropriate, floors must allow adequate surface drainage.	Floors must be designed to prevent pooling of water in normal use. Where there may be significant spillage onto floors or wet cleaning (hoses) is used, floor drains may be provided. In this case the floor levels must fall towards the drains.	(Note that with modern wet-vac machines floor drainage is not always needed).
(b) wall surfaces must be maintained in a sound condition and they must be easy to clean and, where necessary, disinfect. *This will require the use of impervious, non-absorbent, washable and non-toxic materials and require a smooth surface up to a height appropriate for the operations, unless the proprietor of the food business can satisfy the food authority that other materials used are appropriate.*	Walls must be properly maintained so that they can be kept clean. Wall surfaces immediately behind food preparation surfaces or equipment must be able to be disinfected periodically to reduce the risk of food contamination. Assuming that they are properly installed, wall surfaces that would comply with this requirement include: Washable painted plaster; Epoxy resin and similar coatings; Ceramic tiles; Stainless Steel sheeting; PVC, GRP and other proprietary sheeting. The wall surface must be cleanable to a height which might be expected to become soiled with food debris under normal operations.	To aid cleaning it is good practice that all junctions between floors and walls and vertical wall angles should be coved. This will usually be to a height of at least 1.80m. Wall surfaces above this height should also be cleanable but need not be so durable.

Legal requirement	Guide to compliance	Advice on good practice
(c) ceilings and overhead fixtures must be designed, constructed and finished to prevent the accumulation of dirt	Ceiling or overhead surfaces that would comply with this requirement, (assuming that they are properly fixed, applied or installed) include: • smooth washable painted plaster • direct fixed ceiling systems • suspended ceilings	Polystyrene or fibre tiles would not be suitable in high humidity locations. The choice and design of ceiling may be important in reducing condensation. Ceilings should allow effective cleaning to take place periodically. There should be access points in suspended ceilings.
and reduce condensation, the growth of undesirable moulds	Any surface must be capable of being cleaned. • the inner surface of a roof structure will provide an acceptable surface provided that it is in a sound state of repair and cleanable. Ceiling materials and design play an important part in reducing condensation in conjunction with the ventilation system.	
and the shedding of particles.	Ceilings must be periodically maintained to remove any mould build-up or any other particles or debris that could fall into food.	
(d) windows and other openings must be constructed to prevent the accumulation of dirt. *Those which can be opened to the outside environment must where necessary be fitted with insect proof screens which can be easily removed for cleaning. Where open windows would result in contamination of foodstuffs, windows must remain closed and fixed during production;*	They must allow effective cleaning and prevent the accumulation of dirt. This does not necessarily require sloping cills to comply with the provision. Windows must be screened if: (a) they open directly into food preparation areas, AND (b) they are opened for ventilation during food preparation, AND (c) screening is necessary to prevent a risk of infestation and/or contamination. Where dirt build-up on insect proof screens may present a risk of food contamination, the screens must be designed to be easily removed for cleaning.	Sloping window cills help to prevent accumulation of dirt. It is good practice to screen all openable windows in food preparation areas.

Legal requirement	Guide to compliance	Advice on good practice

(e) doors must be easy to clean and, where necessary, disinfect.

This will require the use of smooth and non-absorbent surfaces, unless the proprietor of the food business can satisfy the food authority that other materials used are appropriate;

Any door used by staff who handle open food during work activity may be a source of contamination, especially if staff are likely to touch the door with their hands. These doors must be capable of disinfection. Door furniture likely to come into hand contact such as finger plates and handles must also be capable of disinfection.

A variety of smooth impervious surfaces are available. A cleanable paint or sealed finish would comply. Unsealed wood does not comply.

It is good practice that doors should be flush design to avoid angles and mouldings that accumulate dirt.

Swing doors with kick plates or push plates are preferable to doors with handles.

(f) surfaces (including surfaces of equipment) in contact with food must be maintained in a sound condition and be easy to clean and, where necessary, disinfect. This will require the use of smooth, washable and non-toxic materials, unless the proprietor of the food business can satisfy the food authority that other materials used are appropriate.

This provision covers food preparation surfaces and worktops that come into direct contact with food. Also food contact surfaces of equipment. Other surfaces that do not normally come into direct contact with food but are in close proximity could contaminate food if dirty, for example the outer casings of equipment. These surfaces must also comply.

Food contact surfaces must be maintained in good condition so that they are easily cleaned. All surfaces that come into contact with high risk foods must be able to be disinfected regularly.

Surfaces which would comply with this requirement (assuming that they are properly fixed, applied or installed and maintained) include:

- Stainless steel
- Ceramics
- Food grade plastics

Wooden boards are inappropriate for cutting of high risk foods.

[NOTE: There are further requirements for the hygiene of Equipment in Chapter V]

[NOTE: This regulation is about having equipment that *can* be cleaned and disinfected. The requirement actually to do so is found in Chapters V & IX.]

Joins between horizontal work surfaces could present a dirt trap. Continuous surfaces are better, or joins that are properly sealed, or abutting surfaces that can be separated for cleaning.

Legal requirement	Guide to compliance	Advice on good practice

2 Where necessary, adequate facilities must be provided for the cleaning and disinfecting of work tools and equipment.

These facilities must be constructed of materials resistant to corrosion and must be easy to clean and have an adequate supply of hot and cold water.

It will be necessary to clean all equipment from time to time depending upon how it is used and the types of food that it is used for. Containers used to hold dry ingredients will be cleaned fairly infrequently. Equipment that comes into direct contact with 'high risk' foods will be cleaned and disinfected much more often.

Facilities must be provided to clean and disinfect all tools and equipment, crockery, cutlery, glasses and serving dishes that come into contact with food.

Suitable equipment will include:

- Sinks together with detergents and disinfectants for manual equipment cleaning. (Sinks must be large enough to deal with the equipment normally used in the premises)
- Sterilising sinks
- Automatic spray wash machines (dishwashers)
- Hoses or other equipment for cleaning and disinfection of fixed equipment.

There must be enough equipment to suit the size of the facility.

DRYING of equipment must not cause recontamination, for example from soiled cloths. Space for air drying of equipment is a suitable alternative.

Equipment must be of durable construction and resistant to corrosion, especially those that will come into contact with powerful cleaning chemicals.

A single mixer tap is acceptable, or water supplied at a regulated temperature from a heating unit.

It is good practice to provide facilities for draining and drying of equipment close to the area where it is washed.

Drying cloths will ideally be single use.

Where crockery, glasses and cutlery are washed by hand, it is good practice to use a food approved detergent and disinfectant. It is good practice in larger operations to use mechanical dish, glass or pot wash. (Back up facilities should be available in case of breakdown).

Twin sinks are preferable to allow washing and rinsing.

Cleaning chemicals brought into food rooms for use should be handled carefully to prevent contamination of food.

Legal requirement	Guide to compliance	Advice on good practice
3 Where appropriate, adequate provision must be made for any necessary washing of the food.	Separate sinks must be provided for food preparation and equipment washing if the volume of preparation in the kitchen demands it. In smaller operations, one sink may be used for both equipment and food washing, provided that both activities can be done effectively and without prejudice to food safety. If the same sink is to be used at different times for both food preparation and equipment washing, it should be thoroughly cleaned between each process.	It is good practice to have signs above sinks indicating what they can be used for.
Every sink or other facility for the washing of food must have an adequate supply of hot and/or cold potable water as required, and be kept clean.	Hot water supply is not essential if a sink is to be used exclusively for food preparation. A single mixer tap is acceptable, or water supplied at a regulated temperature from a heating unit.	

Part 4   The 'Rules of hygiene'

Chapter III   Requirements for movable and/or temporary premises (such as marquees, market stalls, mobile sales vehicles), premises used primarily as a private dwelling house, premises used occasionally for catering purposes and vending machines

Introduction

Three situations will be tackled separately under this chapter as different practicalities apply.

A   Mobile and/or temporary premises and premises used occasionally for commercial food preparation

In some cases separate guidance is given on mobiles or temporary premises.

Premises used occasionally (for example church halls, village halls, etc) must follow the guidance for temporary premises. Anyone using these premises must have regard for other activities that have taken place in the premises. If these may present a risk of food contamination, the premises should be thoroughly cleaned and if necessary disinfected before commercial food preparation begins.

(Note that the responsibility to produce safe food remains with the proprietor of the commercial food operation, not with the manager or hirer of the premises).

Boats on inland waterways used for commercial catering will be regarded as mobile premises.

Further guidance on good practice is available from the Mobile and Outdoor Caterers Association of Great Britain*, and in the National Guidelines for Outdoor Catering* available from the Chartered Institute of Environmental Health.

B   Vending machines

Preparation and storage of food for vending machines will take place either in catering premises which comply with the remainder of this guide, or in food manufacturing premises which are covered by appropriate guides or regulations. This section will only deal with issues related to the point of sale merchandiser.

C   Domestic premises

These will be treated as a third group. Additional guidance on good practice is given in the LACOTS* guide issued June 1994.

*[Contact addresses are given in Part 6.]

In provision 2 of sections A, B, and C the guide to compliance indicates what is considered to be necessary to comply with the provision in a catering situation. Clearly, all provisions are not applicable to all situations. For example, the need to make 'adequate provision for the cleaning of foodstuffs' will not be applicable when food is not cleaned in the course of the operation, such as an ice cream van. It is only necessary to comply with provisions that are applicable.

A   Mobile and Temporary premises

Points apply to both mobile or temporary premises unless separate guidance is given.

Legal requirement	Guide to compliance	Advice on good practice
1 Premises shall be so sited, designed, constructed and kept clean and maintained in good repair and condition, as to avoid the risk of contaminating foodstuffs and harbouring pests, so far as is reasonably practicable.	**Siting** Must not be sited close to sources of contamination or pests. For example, it may not be acceptable to locate temporary or mobile premises close to refuse tips or a source of airborne emissions that would present risks of infestation &/or contamination. **Design & construction** If the premises cannot be proofed against pest access, then food must not be stored in the temporary premises unless it is in a storage unit or container that itself prevents access of pests. **Kept clean, maintained and in good repair** Food contact surfaces must be cleaned and disinfected frequently. Equipment should be clean and free from contamination before the start of a work session. Other areas where dust or food debris may accumulate must be cleaned periodically.	Where possible, temporary premises should be sited near to key services such as water, drainage and electricity. Tents or marquees should be made of cleanable materials or food preparation areas should have washable linings. It is good practice to have detailed cleaning schedules, see Chapter II (1). It is good practice to dismantle equipment if this allows more effective cleaning.
2 In particular and where necessary: *(a) appropriate facilities must be available to maintain adequate personal hygiene (including facilities for the hygienic washing and drying of hands, hygienic sanitary arrangements and changing facilities);*	There must be a basin or basins used for handwash only, provided with hot and cold water or water at a suitable temperature, soap or detergent and a means of hand drying. In temporary facilities, handwash basins must also be provided close to the toilets. Protective clothing must be provided to meet the standards in Chapter VIII.	Cloth towels which allow the same area of the towel to be reused are not recommended. It is good practice to provide bactericidal detergent. In temporary facilities, it is good practice to provide space and secure storage so that staff can change into work clothes outside the food preparation areas.

Legal requirement	Guide to compliance	Advice on good practice
(b) surfaces in contact with food must be in a sound condition and be easy to clean and, where necessary, disinfect. This will require the use of smooth, washable, non toxic materials, unless the proprietor of the food business can satisfy the food authority that other materials are appropriate;	Surfaces must meet the standards in Chapter II (1)(f).	
(c) adequate provision must be made for the cleaning and where necessary, disinfecting of work utensils and equipment;	Hot and cold water, or water at a suitable controlled temperature, must be available for washing tools and equipment together with a supply of detergent. Equipment may be returned to the caterer's base depot for cleaning. Arrangements must be made for equipment that needs to be cleaned more frequently, for example whilst a mobile unit is away from the base depot, such as knives, tongs, ice cream scoops. Suitable disinfectant should be available for food contact equipment.	It is good practice to use these sinks only for equipment washing. Where this is not practicable, the sink must be cleaned between different activities. Facilities should be available nearby for draining and drying.
(d) adequate provision must be made for the cleaning of food-stuffs;	Similar standards to those in Chapter II, III must apply. For mobiles, facilities for cleaning food may be at the base depot.	It is good practice to use separate sinks for food washing. Where this is not practicable, the sink should be cleaned between different activities.
(e) an adequate supply of hot and/or cold potable water must be available;	Temporary facilities will ideally be connected to a potable supply, preferably the mains water supply. Where this is not practicable, tanked supplies or water bowsers may be used but these, and supplies in mobiles, must comply with the following standards: (i) Must be filled from a potable supply, ideally the mains. (ii) The tank must be kept clean and disinfected frequently. Hot water must be available for the washing of tools and equipment in temporary premises. If private water supplies are used, they must be of potable standard.	It is good practice to empty tanks daily and refill with fresh water. Filling hoses should be kept clean. It is good practice to sterilise the tank with chlorine at least monthly. Tanks should be enclosed or covered. Clean & waste water tanks should be identified.

Legal requirement	Guide to compliance	Advice on good practice
(f) adequate arrangements and/or facilities for the hygienic storage and disposal of hazardous and/or inedible substances and waste (whether liquid or solid) must be available;	Solid waste must be removed frequently from food preparation and storage areas. It must be stored in lidded containers whilst awaiting collection from the site. Liquid waste will ideally be linked into mains drainage. Holding tanks may be used if access to drainage is not available. They must be discharged carefully so that there is no risk of food contamination. They must not be emptied directly on the ground.	If using plastic sacks, it is good practice to 'double bag' to reduce spillage. Storage tanks should be kept clean and disinfected periodically. Sullage pits or soak-aways may also be acceptable if they are constructed and used in a way that does not risk the contamination of food.
(g) adequate facilities and/or arrangements for maintaining and monitoring suitable food temperature conditions must be available;	Specific temperature controls will apply to some foods. Guidance on temperature control is given in Part 5 of this guide. **Chilled storage** Mechanical refrigeration equipment will normally be needed to achieve satisfactory temperatures. In some situations, for very short periods of time, insulated boxes with eutectic plates or ice packs may be effective. **Hot holding** Insulated boxes will only be effective over short periods of time. **In any facility covered by Chapter III there must also be equipment to check that food temperatures are suitable. This may include portable thermometers or temperature readouts built into equipment.**	Note that temperature Regulations relate to food temperatures not the air temperature of equipment. Temperature displays built into equipment may NOT indicate the temperature of FOOD at every part of the unit.
(h) foodstuffs must be so placed as to avoid, so far as is reasonably practicable, the risk of contamination.	Detailed points in Chapter IX will apply. Key points will be: (i) Ready to eat foods must be kept away from raw foods that may contaminate them both in storage and during preparation. (ii) Working surfaces and equipment must be kept clean and disinfected. (iii) People handling food must avoid spreading contamination. (More advice is given in Chapter VIII) When transporting food to temporary premises or premises used occasionally, the conditions described in 2(g), 2(h) and Chapter IV must be followed.	It is good practice to minimise the amount of food preparation in temporary or mobile premises, either by choosing menus that only involve simple cook and serve steps or by arranging more elaborate preparation to be completed in a permanent base kitchen.

B   Vending machines

It is assumed that any preparation of food for vending machines will take place either in catering premises which comply with other Chapters of this guide, or in food manufacturing premises. This section will deal only with the point of sale automatic merchandiser. It is possible that a separate and more detailed guide to compliance for vending and dispensing will be produced.

Legal requirement	Guide to compliance	Advice on good practice
1 *Vending machines shall be so sited, designed, constructed and kept clean and maintained in good repair and condition, as to avoid the risk of contaminating foodstuffs and harbouring pests, so far as is reasonably practicable.*	**Siting** Must be sited in clean areas that are free from pests especially rodents and crawling insects. **Design/construction** Design must avoid angles, recesses and voids that would make cleaning difficult or provide harbourage to pests. Plumbing and water contact parts of drinks vending machines must comply with any relevant local water by-laws. Hot drinks vendors must be designed to prevent steam from affecting dry ingredients. (Obviously design/construction of machines rests with machine manufacturers, but the proprietor of the catering business must ensure that he selects and installs equipment that meets the criteria.) **Kept clean, maintained & in good repair** Food contact surfaces must be cleaned and disinfected regularly. Other areas where dust or food debris may accumulate and attract pests must be cleaned periodically.	It is good practice to site drinks machines in well ventilated areas to avoid build up of condensation. It is good practice to have detailed cleaning schedules. (See Chapter I (1)). It is good practice to dismantle equipment if this allows more effective cleaning.
2 *In particular and where necessary:* *(a) appropriate facilities must be available to maintain adequate personal hygiene (including facilities for the hygienic washing and drying of hands, hygienic sanitary arrangements and changing facilities);*	People responsible for primary food preparation must comply with the appropriate standards in Chapter VIII. Personnel responsible for loading open food into machines and cleaning food contact parts must also comply with standards appropriate to that food. Personnel who only load wrapped food must comply with the standards for delivery driver/storeman in Chapter VIII.	

Legal requirement	Guide to compliance	Advice on good practice
(b) surfaces in contact with food must be in sound condition and be easy to clean and, where necessary, disinfect. This will require the use of smooth, washable, non toxic materials, unless the proprietor of the food business can satisfy the food authority that other materials are appropriate;	The standards in Chapter II (1)(f) will apply.	
(c) adequate provision must be made for the cleaning and where necessary, disinfecting of work utensils and equipment;	A supply of hot and cold potable water must be available for periodic cleaning and disinfection of any machine vending open food.	
(d) adequate provision must be made for the cleaning of foodstuffs;	(This is not applicable to the vending machine).	
(e) an adequate supply of hot and/or cold potable water must be available;	Drinks vending machines must be connected to a supply of water which is of an acceptable quality. Proprietors must ensure that the quality of water does not deteriorate during storage in the machine. Internal pipes and tanks must be kept clean.	Some materials may need to be sterilised periodically. Carbon filters should be changed regularly.
(f) adequate arrangements and/or facilities for the hygienic storage and disposal of hazardous and/or inedible substances and waste (whether liquid or solid) must be available;	(Liquid waste will only involve overspill from certain drinks vending machines). Spoiled or out of date stocks must be removed from the machine for disposal.	It is good practice for the machine design to include a cut off if the overspill bucket is full. The container should be emptied and cleaned as part of the regular cleaning routine.

Legal requirement	Guide to compliance	Advice on good practice
(g) adequate facilities and/or arrangements for maintaining and monitoring suitable food temperature conditions must be available;	Some foods held in vending machines may be subject to temperature control regulations. Guidance on temperature control is given in Part 5 of this guide.

A method of temperature checking must be available.

In Scotland, machines vending chilled meals to be reheated by the vendor may be subject to the 82°C reheat requirement. In this case:

– The reheat equipment must be capable of achieving that temperature.

– The reheat instructions must be designed to achieve that temperature. | Note that temperatures may vary within any storage unit and air temperature measurements are not always a good reflection of food temperatures. If the system of temperature checking involves a sensor measuring air temperature at one point in the unit, this should reflect the 'worst case', e.g. warmest point. |
| *(h) foodstuffs must be so placed as to avoid, so far as is reasonably practicable, the risk of contamination.* | If there is a risk of contamination, wrapping the food may be a practical way of dealing with it. | |

C Domestic premises

This section will deal only with the domestic premises used primarily as a dwelling house but also for commercial food production as part of a catering business. The transport of food and the place at which food is sold or served may be subject to other sections. The suitability of domestic premises for commercial food preparation should be judged against the size of the business and the frequency with which the premises are used. Additional guidance on good practice is given in the LACOTS guide issued June 1994; a contact address is given in Part 6.

Legal requirement	Guide to compliance	Advice on good practice
1 Premises shall be so sited, designed, constructed and kept clean and maintained in good repair and condition, as to avoid the risk of contaminating foodstuffs and harbouring pests, so far as is reasonably practicable.	**Siting, design & construction** Traditional domestic structural finishes may be satisfactory if they can be kept clean and are maintained in good repair. **Kept clean, maintained & in good repair** Food contact surfaces must be cleaned and disinfected regularly . As a minimum standard, they should be clean and disinfected before beginning commercial food preparation. Other areas where dust or food debris may accumulate and attract pests must be cleaned periodically.	It is good practice to have detailed cleaning schedules, [see Chapter II (1)]. It is good practice to dismantle equipment if this allows more effective cleaning.
2 In particular and where necessary: (a) appropriate facilities must be available to maintain adequate personal hygiene (including facilities for the hygienic washing and drying of hands, hygienic sanitary arrangements and changing facilities);	Basins for hand washing must be available together with soap and water and a means of hand drying. Personal hygiene requirements are found in Chapter VIII.	In domestic premises, hand wash basins are likely to be in the bathroom. In premises used frequently for commercial food preparation, an additional hand wash basin in the kitchen is advisable especially if high risk foods are prepared. Towels should be of a type that are not reusable.
(b) surfaces in contact with food must be in sound condition and be easy to clean and, where necessary, disinfect. This will require the use of smooth, washable, non toxic materials, unless the proprietor of the food business can satisfy the food authority that other materials are appropriate;	Surfaces must meet the standards described in Chapter II (1)(f).	It is good practice to follow the advice in Chapter II (1)(f).

Legal requirement	Guide to compliance	Advice on good practice
(c) adequate provision must be made for the cleaning and, where necessary, disinfecting of work utensils and equipment;	A sink with hot & cold water must be available to wash tools and equipment together with a supply of detergent.	The sink for equipment washing will normally be used for food washing as well. It should be cleaned between uses and preferably disinfected. There should be space for drainage and drying. An automatic dishwasher is recommended.
(d) adequate provision must be made for the cleaning of foodstuffs;	Cold potable water must be available in sinks used to wash food.	
(e) an adequate supply of hot and/or cold potable water must be available;	Cold water from the rising main could be expected to satisfy this requirement. If connected to a private supply, the safety and potability of the water may need to be verified. Private Water Supplies Regulations 1991 (or Private Water Supplies [Scotland] Regulations 1992) will apply.	
(f) adequate arrangements and/or facilities for the hygienic storage and disposal of hazardous and/ or inedible substances and waste (whether liquid or solid) must be available;	Food waste must be removed regularly from the kitchen and stored in lidded bins or containers awaiting removal from site.	Food waste may be collected in the kitchen in open transfer bins or sacks. If commercial food preparation creates significant amounts of food waste, arrangements should be made to have it removed more frequently than the normal domestic waste collection.
(g) adequate facilities and/or arrangements for maintaining and monitoring suitable food temperature conditions must be available;	Specific temperature controls will apply to some foods. Guidance on temperature control is given in Part 5 of this guide. The person operating the food business must ensure that suitable equipment is available to achieve good temperature controls for the type of food preparation that is carried out. **Delivery** Appropriate food temperatures must be maintained during transport of food from domestic premises to the place at which it will be served or sold. Guidance on both hot and cold food delivery is given in Chapter IV. **In any facility covered by Chapter III equipment must be available to monitor food temperatures.**	It is good practice to keep all chilled food at 5°C or cooler. Note: Many domestic refrigerators may not achieve consistently the temperatures required by law, especially units that do NOT have fan assisted circulation or which are overloaded.

Legal requirement	Guide to compliance	Advice on good practice
(h) foodstuffs must be so placed as to avoid, so far as is reasonably practicable, the risk of contamination.	Detailed points from Chapter IX apply. Key points will be: (i) Ready to eat foods must be kept away from raw foods that may contaminate them. This will apply during storage, transport and preparation. (ii) Working surfaces and equipment must be kept clean and disinfected. (iii) People handling foods must avoid spreading contamination. (More information in Ch VIII) Domestic activities that present a risk of food contamination such as the access of pets, and the handling of laundry (especially heavily soiled materials and nappies) must not happen at the same time as commercial food preparation, and adequate steps must be taken to clean and disinfect the area before food is produced. In addition, cases of infectious disease affecting other members of the household may present a risk.	It is good practice to minimise the amount of commercial food preparation in domestic premises by choosing menus that involve only simple preparation steps. Domestic premises are unlikely to have adequate facilities to safely pre-cook and cool food except in very small quantities. It would be good practice to consult a GP and/or EHO on the best course of action in the specific cases.

Part 4　The 'Rules of hygiene'

Chapter IV　Transport

Transport of food in the course of a catering operation will apply only to certain specialised types of operation. For example, central production units.

Where food is delivered to a catering outlet, legal compliance will be the responsibility of the supplier. When caterers collect food from wholesalers or cash & carry outlets *they* have the responsibility for its safety and compliance with this regulation. This Chapter will apply in addition to other parts of the regulations, and temperature control regulations.

Legal requirement	Guide to compliance	Advice on good practice
1 *Conveyances and/or containers used for transporting foodstuffs must be kept clean and maintained in good repair and condition in order to protect foodstuffs from contamination, and must, where necessary, be designed and constructed to permit adequate cleaning and/or disinfection.*	Containers may include trolleys, bags, boxes, trays, and crates made of a wide variety of materials. The type of container that will be suitable and the cleaning necessary will depend upon the type of food and its intended use. For example, the wooden crate used to transport raw vegetables to an outdoor event, will not be suitable to transport prepared meals within a cook chill system. Certain foods will be covered by temperature control regulations and transport equipment will need to be designed accordingly. More detail is given in provision 6 of this Chapter.	
2 *(1) Receptacles in vehicles and/ or containers must not be used for transporting anything other than foodstuffs where this may result in contamination of foodstuffs.*	Other materials, such as cleaning chemicals, may be carried with food provided that every care is taken to prevent contamination.	

Legal requirement	Guide to compliance	Advice on good practice
(2) Bulk foodstuffs in liquid, granulate or powder form must be transported in receptacles and/or containers/tankers reserved for the transport of foodstuffs if otherwise there is a risk of contamination. Such containers must be marked in a clearly visible and indelible fashion, in one or more Community languages, to show that they are used for the transport of foodstuffs, or must be marked 'for foodstuffs only'.	This provision is unlikely to apply to catering situations	
3 Where conveyances and/or containers are used for transporting anything in addition to foodstuffs or for transporting different foodstuffs at the same time, there must be effective separation of products, where necessary, to protect against the risk of contamination.	It is necessary to segregate from food anything that may cause contamination. These may be chemicals which taint or are toxic or other foods that are more contaminated, for example raw meat must be separated from cooked ready to eat food. Food and non-food may be delivered at the same time in the same vehicle providing that both are adequately separated and wrapped or packed and that there is no risk of spillage or contact that may contaminate food.	
4 Where conveyances and/or containers have been used for transporting anything other than foodstuffs or for transporting different foodstuffs, there must be effective cleaning between loads to avoid the risk of contamination.	This requirement also depends on the nature of what has been transported and what is to be transported next. The more contaminated the previous load and the more 'high risk' the next, the more thorough the cleaning must be. If the earlier load may have had microbial contamination, for example raw food, or food waste, then cleaning must also include effective disinfection.	
5 Foodstuffs in conveyances and/or containers must be so placed and protected as to minimise the risk of contamination.	Where there is a risk of contamination food must be adequately wrapped and/or separated from other materials in the conveyance.	Adequate packing (see guidance on provision 3) may eliminate the hazard.

Legal requirement	Guide to compliance	Advice on good practice

6 Where necessary, conveyances and/or containers used for transporting foodstuffs, must be capable of maintaining foodstuffs at appropriate temperatures and, where necessary, designed to allow those temperatures to be monitored.

Specific temperature controls will apply to some foods. Guidance on temperature control is given in Part 5 of this guide.

This requirement can be met in a number of ways depending upon the journey, particularly its duration, and how often the container might be opened during the journey.

Mechanical or cryogenic cooling may be needed for longer journeys or multiple drops. Insulated containers may be adequate in other circumstances.

MONITORING would in practice only apply to transport of perishable foodstuffs. This can be achieved either by:

- Thermometers built into vans or containers. (If these are fitted, care must be taken to understand how the reading relates to actual food temperatures.)

- Hand held probes may be used as an acceptable alternative.

Note that the Regulations specify food temperatures, *not* the temperature of food holding equipment.

Home delivery food should be well protected in primary packaging. Insulated containers (or chilled vehicles) should be used to ensure that food is kept at suitable temperatures during the journey.

When temperature control during transport depends only upon insulation, it is good practice to ensure that food is properly cooled or heated before dispatch.

Part 4   The 'Rules of hygiene'

Chapter V   Equipment requirements

Legal requirement	Guide to compliance	Advice on good practice
1 *All articles, fittings and equipment with which food comes into contact shall be kept clean and:* *(a) be so constructed, be of such materials, and be kept in such good order, repair and condition, as to minimise any risk of contamination of the food;*	This will relate to work surfaces, food processing equipment, and any other fittings that may come into contact with food. 'Contact' will mean direct contact or such close proximity to food that it may transfer contamination. This will also include crockery, cutlery and glassware. These must all be kept clean. The degree of cleaning will depend upon the use to which the equipment is put, for example the standard of cleaning of a food slicer is more critical than that of a potato peeler. Equipment must be regularly cleaned. Where possible it should be dismantled as far as necessary to allow this to be done effectively. When equipment or surfaces come into contact with 'high risk' food, cleaning must include disinfection. Materials that comply include: ● Stainless steel. ● Food grade plastics and laminates. (These are suitable for food contact surfaces and heavy equipment). ● Aluminium and tinned copper (Acceptable but are less durable). ● Crockery and cutlery are available in a variety of suitable materials. ● Wood is inappropriate for use with 'high risk' foods. Equipment must not be used when its condition has deteriorated to the point that it cannot be effectively cleaned or it poses a foreign body hazard or any other risk of contamination. **[Note: points on hygienic structure and design of new equipment are included in The Supply of Machinery (Safety) Regulations 1992]**	Unsealed wood or galvanised equipment is not recommended for any situation where open food is involved. Cleaning instructions are usually supplied by manufacturers. It is good practice that equipment should be designed to allow easy dismantling that provides access to all parts that need cleaning. Equipment that is no longer used should be removed from the food premises.

Legal requirement	Guide to compliance	Advice on good practice
(b) with the exception of non-returnable containers and packaging, be so constructed, be of such materials, and be kept in such good order, repair and condition, as to enable them to be kept thoroughly cleaned and, where necessary, disinfected, sufficient for the purposes intended;	Food equipment, work surfaces and fittings must be designed with smooth, durable surfaces to allow effective cleaning and disinfection. All surfaces that come into contact with 'high risk' food must be able to be disinfected.	Design should avoid sharp angles and ledges. Joints should be finished at a curved radius. It is recommended that each piece of equipment has a detailed cleaning schedule. (See Chapter I (1).) It is good practice to disinfect all food equipment regularly even if it used for 'low risk' applications.
(c) be installed in such a manner as to allow adequate cleaning of the surrounding area;	The criterion is cleanability. Installation should allow access for effective cleaning. Alternatively equipment must be mobile to enable adequate cleaning and disinfection. The amount and type of cleaning needed will relate to the area of the premises and the use to which it is put.	Heavy equipment should not be fixed in place in such a way that restricts access for cleaning. Services should not restrict mobility.

Part 4   The 'Rules of hygiene'

Chapter VI   Food Waste

Legal requirement	Guide to compliance	Advice on good practice
1 *Food waste and other refuse must not be allowed to accumulate in food rooms, except so far as is unavoidable for the proper functioning of the business.*	Systems of operation must ensure that refuse containers in food rooms do not become over full and are regularly emptied and removed from the room. (A certain amount of working debris is inevitable in kitchens especially at peak periods).	It is good practice to remove all waste from the food room at the end of day.
2 *Food waste and other refuse must be deposited in closable containers unless the proprietor of the food business can satisfy the food authority that other types of containers used are appropriate. These containers must be of an appropriate construction, kept in sound condition, and where necessary be easy to clean and disinfect.*	Lids on refuse containers used for temporary storage of waste in food preparation areas are not required. They are frequently touched by the hands of food handlers and may be a serious source of contamination. Lids are not required on these waste transfer bins or sack holders. Containers must be constructed of durable material which make them easy to clean and disinfect . Any refuse containers used for STORAGE of waste awaiting collection and removal from site should have a lid, be constructed of a durable material which makes them easy to clean and disinfect. All waste bins must be capable of being cleaned regularly and disinfected periodically. Bins or sack holders used in areas preparing high risk foods must be disinfected more frequently.	Cleaning schedules should ensure that refuse containers are frequently cleaned and disinfected inside and outside. All refuse containers should be easy to move about the food rooms and of a suitable height for easy and comfortable use at work benches. It is desirable that all refuse containers should be lined with plastic liners which can be easily removed and secured to ensure that the minimum of food waste comes into contact with the container. It is good practice to store bagged rubbish either in a bin or a secure area to prevent pecking or gnawing by vermin.

Legal requirement	Guide to compliance	Advice on good practice
3 Adequate provision must be made for the removal and storage of food waste and other refuse. Refuse stores must be designed and managed in such a way as to enable them to be kept clean, and to protect against access by pests, and against contamination of food, drinking water, equipment or premises.	Provision must include frequent removal at the end of each trading session from the immediate food preparation area and arrangements for disposal or collection. The frequency of collection will depend upon the volume and type of waste. Better waste storage facilities may allow less frequent collection. Areas designated or used for the storage of waste must satisfy the requirements of this provision. Areas for indoor storage of refuse must be away from food rooms and be cleared at frequent intervals. Proofing against pest access can be achieved either by storing in a covered area sealed against pest access, or using firmly lidded bins. Liquid food waste such as oil and cleaning chemicals must be disposed of safely. It will not normally be acceptable to flush significant quantities into the drain.	Waste disposal units can provide a hygienic method of disposal of food waste but may need the agreement of the local water company. Outdoor refuse storage should not be sited next to the main delivery entrance where food is brought into the premises. It is good practice to have a separate area designated for outdoor waste storage areas with hard standing and well lit. There should be a hose for cleaning and drainage.

Part 4   The 'Rules of hygiene'

Chapter VII   Water Supply

Legal requirement	Guide to compliance	Advice on good practice
1 There must be an adequate supply of potable water. *This potable water must be used whenever necessary to ensure foodstuffs are not contaminated.*	Potable water must be used: ● for the cleaning of food ● for inclusion in food recipes ● for cleaning of food equipment ● for cleaning surfaces that come into contact with food or the hands of food handlers ● for hand washing Generally, it can be assumed that water will be potable if it comes direct from the water undertakers mains supply or from a storage system that meets the relevent requirements of any local water bye-laws. If the operation has a private water supply, that supply must be of potable quality. Private Water Supplies Regulations 1991 (Scotland 1992) apply. Non potable water may be used where this will not affect the safety and wholesomeness of the food.	Water softeners and water filters, should be maintained in good condition so that they do not contaminate water. Filter cartridges should be changed regularly in accordance with makers instructions. Softened water may not be suitable for infant foods or adults with certain medical conditions.
2 Where appropriate, ice must be made from potable water. This ice must be used whenever necessary to ensure foodstuffs are not contaminated. It must be made, handled and stored under conditions which protect it from all contamination.	All ice to be used in food and drink must be made from potable water. Ice used to cool open food in buffet displays must also be made from potable water. [It is possible to use non-potable water or indeed other liquids in sealed eutectic packs or plates that will only be used for cooling of food and which do not involve any contact between the food itself and the ice inside the pack.] Ice machines must sited away from sources of contamination and be regularly cleaned as should containers and utensils used to store and dispense ice. Parts of the machine and utensils that come into direct contact with ice must be disinfected periodically. Utensils must be made of durable materials that will not present a foreign body hazard from brittle fracture.	Ice for drinks should not be handled with bare hands. Glassware should not be used to 'shovel' ice.

Legal requirement	Guide to compliance	Advice on good practice
3 Steam used directly in contact with food must not contain any substance which presents a hazard to health, or is likely to contaminate the product.	Potable water must be used if the steam may come into contact with, or become included in the food.	
4 Water unfit for drinking used for the generation of steam, refrigeration, fire control and other similar purposes not relating to food, must be conducted in separate systems, readily identifiable and having no connection with, nor any possibility of reflux into, the potable water systems.	Supplies of non-potable water to food preparation areas are not recommended. In some circumstances, hoses for fire fighting may be linked to a supply of water that is not potable. In those cases, the supply should be clearly marked for firefighting and hoses should not be used for cleaning.	

Part 4 The 'Rules of hygiene'

Chapter VIII Personal Hygiene

Legal requirement

1 Every person working in a food handling area shall maintain a high degree of personal cleanliness and shall wear suitable, clean and, where appropriate, protective clothing.

Guide to compliance

- Note that the requirement applies to 'every person'.
- 'Personal cleanliness' is taken to include hygienic practices and habits which, if unsatisfactory, may expose food to the risk of contamination.
- Clothing must be clean and should be changed regularly to maintain hygienic standards to protect the food from risk of contamination.

[Regulation 4 places the onus on the proprietor of the business to ensure that these requirements are complied with.]

Standards of clothing may differ depending upon the duties carried out. The following would fulfill the requirement:
- Personnel preparing open food – clean coat, tunic, uniform or similar, plus head covering
- Storeman/Driver – clean coat or over-garment
- Waiters/waitresses/bar staff – clean clothing, tunic or uniform

Persons working in food handling areas must also practice good hygiene.
They must for example:
- have clean hands if they are handling food.
- not smoke or spit in the food handling area.
- not eat or drink whilst handling food.*
- cover wounds likely to cause risk of contamination of foods (on hands or other exposed parts of the body) with waterproof dressings.
- not wear jewellery or false nails that may present a risk of contamination.

* It is acceptable for cooks to taste dishes during their preparation provided this does not contaminate food.

Advice on good practice

It is good practice for *ALL* visitors to the kitchen(including maintenance personnel) to wear protective clothing and hats if they present a risk of contamination.

Staff who will prepare 'high risk' foods should not travel to their place of work in their protective clothing. They should also remove protective clothing if they leave the premises for other reasons, for example to smoke.

It is good practice to use brightly coloured wound dressings that are easy to spot if they come off.

Persons handling open food should:
- not wear nail varnish
- have short nails
- have clean hair tied back and covered
- wash hands frequently in running water.

Jewellery: sleepers in pierced ears and a plain wedding band are acceptable. Watches should not be worn.

Legal requirement	Guide to compliance	Advice on good practice

2   No person, known or suspected to be suffering from, or to be a carrier of, a disease likely to be transmitted through food or while afflicted, for example with infected wounds, skin infections, sores or with diarrhoea, shall be permitted to work in any food handling area in any capacity in which there is any likelihood of directly or indirectly contaminating food with pathogenic micro-organisms.

When a proprietor becomes aware that a member of staff is suffering from one of the conditions listed, they have the legal responsibility to take the necessary action. This may involve exclusion from work altogether, or exclusion from certain jobs.

Separately, under Regulation 5, any person working in a food handling area must report certain illnesses or conditions to the proprietor where there is any likelihood of them directly or indirectly contaminating food. They must immediately report if they:

- know or suspect that they are suffering from or are a carrier of a disease likely to be transmitted through food

- are afflicted with an infected wound, a skin infection, sores, diarrhoea or any analogous medical condition such as stomach upset or vomiting.

It is good practice for the proprietor to instruct all staff on appointment that they must notify their manager or supervisor if they ever suffer from any of these ailments. It is good practice to give new staff this instruction in writing.

The manager or supervisor should be notified at the beginning of the shift before they start work.

It is good practice for the manager to consult either a medical practitioner or an EHO for advice on the exclusion of the staff member from food handling and on their suitability to return after illness.

Much more detailed guidance is given in the document 'Fitness to Work' from the Department of Health.

A medical questionnaire may be used on appointment. A specimen is given in 'Fitness to Work'.

Part 4   The 'Rules of hygiene'

Chapter IX   Provisions applicable to foodstuffs

Legal requirement	Guide to compliance	Advice on good practice
1 No raw materials or ingredients shall be accepted by a food business if they are known to be, or might reasonably be expected to be, so contaminated with parasites, pathogenic micro-organisms, or toxic, decomposed or foreign substances, that after normal sorting and/or preparatory or processing procedures hygienically applied by food businesses, they would still be unfit for human consumption.	Routine checks must be made periodically on deliveries of food. Different foods will need to be checked more frequently depending upon the degree of risk that they present. For example chickens are more critical than cherries. Critical steps and controls will be identified by the systems described in Part 2. The consignment or a representative sample should be examined to ensure that it is fit for the purpose intended. Checks will determine the general condition of food and may include more specific checks such as date marks or temperature. Unfit food or 'Use By' expired product must not be accepted. It must be immediately returned on the delivery vehicle or set aside and clearly marked for later disposal.	For chilled or frozen foods, checks should be made that food is delivered at the correct temperature. For prepacked foods labelled with 'Use By' date marks, the product should have enough residual life to allow the food to be used within the date. For quality reasons, 'best before' dates should also be checked. Where possible, the competence of suppliers to handle and deliver foods safely should be checked.

Legal requirement	Guide to compliance	Advice on good practice

Legal requirement

2   Raw materials and ingredients stored in the establishment shall be kept in appropriate conditions designed to prevent harmful deterioration and to protect them from contamination.

Guide to compliance

Dry goods storage: Will include the storage of a range of ingredients, fruit and vegetables, dried foods including pasta, cereals and seasonings, and canned or bottled foods.

Areas used should be kept clean and tidy to minimise 'foreign body' hazards and to prevent harbourage of pests.

Packs should be handled with reasonable care to prevent damage to packing that may allow contamination of the food (especially hermetically sealed containers and cans).

Non food items may present a safety hazard if they contaminate food (e.g. cleaning materials). These should be stored away from food and packed in such a way that they cannot contaminate the food.

Chilled Stores: Must be run at suitable temperatures to comply with temperature control regulations. Guidance on temperature control is given in Part 5 of this guide. Note that regulations relate to the temperature of the food, not the air temperature of the storage equipment.

To comply with Food Labelling Regulations food labelled with 'Use By' date marks must be used by the expiry date.

Advice on good practice

Very high ambient temperatures and high humidity should be avoided.

Part used packs or 'broken stock' should be adequately resealed to prevent contamination.

In some cases, it may be better to transfer the stock to lidded bins or other suitable containers. For example, part used canned food should not be kept in the can.

Good stock rotation of dry goods may be important to food quality but it is rarely a food safety issue.

Packaging and wrapping materials and catering disposables to be used for food should also be kept in clean and dry stores that are free from pests and other sources of contamination.

Chilled Stores: It is good practice to have a system of monitoring to check operating temperatures.

Raw food which may be contaminated should be stored away from ready to eat foods. If both have to be kept in the same chiller, they should be kept apart and/or wrapped to prevent cross-contamination, raw on shelves below cooked.

Frozen Stores: Good frozen storage may be important to food quality. Provided frozen food is not thawed and refrozen, it is NOT a food safety issue.

It is good practice to keep frozen stores at the correct temperature (at –18°C or colder), to have a system of temperature monitoring and also to ensure good stock rotation of food within the 'Best Before' dates.

Legal requirement	Guide to compliance	Advice on good practice

Legal requirement

3 All food which is handled, stored, packaged, displayed and transported, shall be protected against any contamination likely to render the food unfit for human consumption,

injurious to health

or contaminated in such a way that it would be unreasonable to expect it to be consumed in that state. In particular, food must be so placed and/or protected as to minimise any risk of contamination.

Guide to compliance

- Food would be 'unfit for human consumption' if it was putrid or toxic or if, for example it contained very unpleasant foreign material. Meat would be unfit if it was taken from animals slaughtered in a knackers yard.

- Food would be 'injurious to health' if it was contaminated with toxic materials or pathogenic micro-organisms at levels which may cause harm in a substantial part of the population. It could be 'unfit' even if the harm were cumulative or only became apparent over a long period of time. An ingredient which showed up as an intolerant reaction in only a few individuals would not be covered.

- Food would be 'contaminated in such a way that it would be unreasonable to expect it to be consumed in that state' if it contained, for example, substantial residues of antibiotics, or unpleasant foreign material, or significant solvent residues.

Protection against these risks will depend upon:

- the potential hazard
- the type of food and how it will be handled

Some hazards (for example toxic material or glass) may immediately render the food 'unfit' or 'injurious to health'. For these hazards, steps must be taken to avoid primary contamination.

For many other hazards, especially food poisoning bacteria, preventing risk will have two elements:

- protection from initial contamination

- protection from multiplication to high numbers that may be infective or toxic.

'Protection' may be achieved by control of either or both of the elements. That is, food may either be protected from contamination and/or held for a short period of time or kept chilled.

Advice on good practice

The design of display equipment (especially self service) can be important in removing other contamination hazards. For example, displays that avoid reaching across food.

'Sneeze screens' may play a small part in reducing airborne contamination.

It is also good practice to prevent handles of utensils from falling into the food. One way of achieving this is to use tools with handles longer than the bowls.

Domestic animals should be kept out of food preparation and serving areas during trading periods.

Laundry operations should be kept separate from kitchens and food stores.

Legal requirement	Guide to compliance	Advice on good practice
3 (Continued)	For example, 'High Risk' food produced in advance, such as in a cook-chill system, will need more rigorous control of primary contamination, because it is intended to be held for several days, albeit at chilled temperature. [Note that there are some food poisoning bacteria and viruses that are infective in low doses. Where there is a specific risk from such a hazard, protection from contamination is the single element.]	
Adequate procedures must be in place to ensure pests are controlled.	This provision includes control of the following pests: insects, rats, mice, and birds.	Procedures which should be taken to control pests could include: • proofing of entrances and other access points • insect screens • electronic fly killers • good stock rotation of dry goods • regular surveys by competent contractors • baiting with pesticides
4 *Hazardous and/or inedible substances, including animal feed-stuffs, shall be adequately labelled and stored in separate and secure containers*	Food that has become spoiled or food that is past its 'Use By' date must be removed from the food room and/or clearly marked so that it cannot be mistaken for wholesome food. It must be kept well away from wholesome food if there is a risk of contamination or taint. In a very few catering premises animals may be kept either as pets or for security. (For example in smaller operations, pubs, and guest houses, with residential accommodation in the same premises). Cleaning materials must be clearly labelled, stored in suitably robust containers, and stored away from food. Under no circumstances should cleaning materials or other hazardous substances be decanted into food containers.	Ideally, pet food will be stored separately from food for the catering operation. If this is not possible, pet food must be clearly labelled and wrapped so that it does not present a risk of contamination.

Part 5 Temperature Controls

This section provides guidance on Food Safety (Temperature Control) Regulations 1995 (SI No. 2200). Regulations 4 to 12 cover the arrangements for **England and Wales.** Similar provisions apply in Northern Ireland.

The requirements that apply to **Scotland** (Regulations 13 to 16) are quite different to those in England and Wales. They are effectively the same Regulations that have applied in Scotland for many years with the addition of the general requirement from the Food Hygiene Directive 93/43/EEC (at Regulation 16).

Note that the general requirement (Regulation 10 in England and Wales, Regulation 16 in Scotland) is over-arching.

The legal requirement for chilled food in England & Wales is established at 8°C by Regulation 4. This guideline follows a principle that 8°C is the formal legal requirement but we recommend throughout that it is good practice to set fridges to keep food at 5°C or cooler to allow a margin of error below the legal standard.

Note that all the temperature control provisions relate to the temperature of the FOOD and not the air temperature of the holding unit. When checking temperatures, care should be taken to make sure that the readings taken represent the FOOD temperature in all parts of the holding unit. This should be borne in mind before relying upon temperature readouts fitted to refrigeration or other temperature controlled equipment.

HAZARD ANALYSIS : The temperature controls demanded by these Regulations will often correspond to important control points from the 'Hazard Analysis' required by Regulation 4(3) of the Food Safety (General Food Hygiene) Regulations 1995.

Practical guidance on temperature control was given in the publication 'Guidelines for the Catering Industry on the Food Hygiene (Amendment) Regulations 1990/91'. This publication is effectively obsolete with the repeal of those Regulations but much of the practical advice remains sound. A revised version of this advice is reproduced as an Annex to this guide. *Note that this does not form part of the guide to compliance with the regulations.*

Compliance with the Temperature Control Regulations
SUMMARY OF PROVISIONS

ENGLAND & WALES

Reg.	Requirement	Comments
4	Chilled food must be kept at 8°C or cooler.	Applies only to foods that would become unsafe.
5	Various cold foods are exempt: shelf stable, canned, raw materials, cheeses during ripening, and others where there is no risk to health.	Soft cheeses once ripe, and perishable food from opened cans must be kept below 8°C.
6	Manufacturers may recommend higher storage temperature/shorter storage life (provided that safety is verified).	Caterers must use the food within the 'Use By' date indicated.
7(1)	Cold food on display or for service can be warmer than 8°C. Maximum of 4 hours is allowed.	Any item of food can be displayed outside temperature control only once. The burden of proof is on the caterer.
7(2)	Tolerances outside of temperature control are also allowed during transfer or preparation of food, and defrost or breakdown of equipment.	No time/temperature limits specified. Both should be minimized consistent with food safety.
8 / 9	Hot food should be kept at 63°C or hotter.	Food may be kept at a temperature cooler than 63°C for maximum 2 hours if it is for service or on display.
10	A general requirement for all food to be kept under temperature control if that is needed to keep it safe.	Applies to raw materials and foods in preparation. Limited periods outside temperature control are permitted for certain practicalities. No temperature is specified. A combination of time & temperature will be important.
11	Food must be cooled quickly after heating or preparation.	No limits are specified - must be consistent with food safety.

SCOTLAND

Reg.	Requirement	Comments
13	Cold food must be kept in a cool place or refrigerator	No temperature is specified.
13	Hot food must be kept at 63°C or hotter.	There are exemptions for food on display, during preparation, etc.
14	Food that is reheated must reach 82°C.	Exemption if 82°C detrimental to food quality.
15	Gelatin must be boiled, or held at 71°C for at least 30 minutes.	Unused glaze must be chilled quickly and kept in a refrigerator.
16	A general requirement similar to England & Wales, Reg. 10. for all food to be kept under temperature control if that is needed to keep it safe. Additionally includes the need for rapid cooling.	Applies to raw materials and foods in preparation. Limited periods outside temperature control are permitted for certain practicalities. No temperature is specified. A combination of time & temperature will be important.

Note that all temperatures specified are FOOD temperatures *not* the air temperature of refrigerators, vehicles or hot cabinets.

Section 1 England & Wales (Regulations 4-12)

Legal requirement	Guide to compliance	Advice on good practice
Reg. 4(1) Subject to para. (2) and reg. 5, no person shall keep any food - *(a) which is likely to support the growth of pathogenic micro-organisms or the formation of toxins; and* *(b) with respect to which any commercial operation is being carried out,* *at or in food premises at a temperature above 8°C.*	This regulation only applies to food that will support the growth of pathogenic micro-organisms. Such foods must be kept at 8°C or cooler. The types of food that will be subject to temperature control are indicated in the table below.	It is good practice to keep some foods at temperatures lower than 8°C either to preserve quality or to allow longer term storage. It is good practice to set fridges at a target food temperature of 5°C to allow a margin of error below the legal standard. Particularly cabinet fridges where there can be significant temperature rises during frequent door opening.

Foods that are likely to be subject to temperature control

Food Type	Comments
Cooked meats and fish, meat and fish products.	Includes prepared meals, meat pies, pâtés, potted meats, quiches and similar dishes based on fish.
Cooked meats in cans which have been pasteurised rather than fully sterilised.	Typically large catering packs of ham or cured shoulder.
Cooked vegetable dishes.	Includes cereals, rice & pulses.
Any cooked dish containing egg or cheese.	Includes flans, pastries etc.
	Some cooked vegetable or dessert recipes may have sufficiently high sugar content* (possibly combined with other factors like acidity) to prevent the growth of pathogenic bacteria. These will not be subject to mandatory temperature control.
Prepared salads and dressings.	Includes mayonnaise and prepared salads with mayonnaise or any other style of dressing. Some salads or dressings may have a formulation (especially the level of acidity**) that is adequate to prevent growth of pathogens.
Soft cheeses / mould ripened cheeses (after ripening).	Cheeses will include Camembert, Brie, Stilton, Roquefort, Danish Blue and any similar style of cheese.
Smoked or cured fish, and raw scombroid fish.	For example smoked salmon, smoked trout, smoked mackerel, etc. Also raw tuna, mackerel and other scombroid fish.
Any sandwiches whose fillings include any of these types of food.	
Low acid** desserts and cream products.	Includes dairy desserts, fromage frais and cream cakes. *Some artificial cream may be 'ambient stable' due to low water activity and/or high sugar. Any product that does NOT support the growth of pathogenic micro-organisms does NOT have to be kept below 8°C. It may be necessary to get clarification from suppliers.*
Fresh pasta and uncooked or partly cooked pasta and dough products.	Includes unbaked pies and sausage rolls, unbaked pizzas and fresh pasta.
Smoked or cured meats which are not ambient stable.	Salami, parma hams and other fermented meats will *not* be subject to temperature controls if they are ambient shelf stable.

* Technically, aW (water activity) is the key criterion.

**Technically, pH 4.5 (or more acid) is the critical limit. (See Glossary)

Legal requirement	Guide to compliance	Advice on good practice

Reg. 4(2) Para. (1) shall not apply to any food which, as part of a mail order transaction, is being conveyed by post or by a private or common carrier to an ultimate consumer.

Reg. 4(3) Subject to Reg. 5, no person shall supply by mail order any food which -

(a) is likely to support the growth of pathogenic micro-organisms or the formation of toxins; and

(b) is being or has been conveyed by post or by private or common carrier to an ultimate consumer, at a temperature which has given rise to or is likely to give rise to a risk to health .

This guide does not cover mail order foods.

The regulation gives exemption from temperature controls for foods delivered by mail order. But only when they are delivered direct to the 'ultimate consumer'. Under these Regulations, Caterers are <u>not</u> 'ultimate consumers' by the definition in Regulation 2. So foods described in 4(1) must be delivered to caterers at the correct temperature, whatever the form of delivery.

Unless a caterer can be assured that perishable foods delivered by mail order arrive in a safe condition (for example, they have not been subject to unacceptable temperature control conditions in transit) then it is not good practice to accept delivery of these foods by mail order.

(Other foods which are not included in 4(1) such as coffee, biscuits, canned foods do not need temperature control and may be delivered by mail order).

Food Safety (Temperature Control) Regulations 1995 - Guide to compliance by Caterers

Legal requirement	Guide to compliance	Advice on good practice
Reg. 5 : Reg. 4 shall not apply to - *(a) food which -* *(i) has been cooked or reheated,* *(ii) is for service or on display for sale, and* *(iii) needs to be kept hot in order to control the growth of pathogenic micro-organisms or the formation of toxins;*	This regulation provides exemption from 8°C holding for certain foods or certain circumstances as described below: a) Food intended to be served HOT is covered by regulation 8.	*In some categories of food there may be some products which are shelf stable but others which must have chilled storage. This will depend upon the formulation of the actual product. For example, amongst sauces, ketchup will invariably be shelf stable, but some mayonnaise recipes may have less acidity and may need chilled storage.*
(b) food which, for the duration of its shelf life, may be kept at ambient temperatures with no risk to health;	b) Some perishable foods can be kept at ambient temperatures for the duration of their shelf life with no risk to health. This may be because they are intended to be kept for only very short periods, or because they have been packed or processed in a certain way. Certain bakery products may benefit from specific exemptions stemming from this provision. These are detailed in the guide for the baking industry.	
(c) food which is being or has been subjected to a process such as dehydration or canning intended to prevent the growth of pathogenic micro-organisms at ambient temperatures, but this paragraph shall cease to apply in circumstances where - *(i) after or by virtue of that process the food was contained in a hermetically sealed container, and* *(ii) that container has been opened;*	c) Canned or similarly processed food need not be kept chilled until the hermetically sealed pack is opened. ● Perishable food of the type mentioned in 4(1) must then be kept chilled (for example corned beef, beans, canned fish, UHT packed milk and dairy products). ● Some canned meats do NOT undergo a full sterilisation process. (Large catering packs of ham or pork shoulder). These must be kept chilled even in the unopened can.	*High acid canned or preserved foods (some fruit, tomatoes, etc.) do not have to be chilled after opening for safety reasons. It is advisable to remove these from the can for storage to avoid any chemical reaction with the metal can body.*
(d) food which must be ripened or matured at ambient temperatures, but this paragraph shall cease to apply once the process of ripening or maturation is completed;	d) Foods which go through a ripening process need not be kept chilled until they are ripe. This applies to mould ripened soft cheeses.	*These cheeses will normally be ripe by the time they are delivered to a caterer and they should be stored at 8°C or cooler.*

5: Temperature Controls

Legal requirement	Guide to compliance	Advice on good practice
(e) raw food intended for further processing (which includes cooking) before human consumption, but only if that processing, if undertaken correctly, will render that food fit for human consumption;	e) Any raw food for further processing does not have to be kept at 8°C or cooler. This will exempt raw meat, poultry and fish. (The further processing must be adequate to eliminate any hazard.) ● Processed foods MUST be kept at 8°C or cooler even if they are to be heated again. (Unless other exemptions apply, either from this Regulation or from Regulations 7, 8 or 9.) ● Raw meat or fish which is intended to be eaten *without* further processing (for example beef for steak tartare, or fish for sushi) will *not* be exempted by this provision. It must be kept chilled. ● Raw scombroid fish (tuna, mackerel, etc.) will also not be exempted by this provision. The 'scombrotoxin' is heat stable and processing will not render contaminated food fit for consumption. Scombroid fish must be kept at 8°C or cooler.	It is good practice to keep raw meat, poultry and fish at 5°C or cooler for the following reasons: ● to preserve quality ● to prevent the growth of spoilage organisms and preserve shelf life ● to prevent the growth of pathogens such as Salmonella. (Although these should be eliminated by correct processing, it is good practice to minimise the bacteria load and reduce the risk that sub-optimal processing will leave the food contaminated.)
(f) food to which Council Regulation (EEC) No 1906/90 on certain marketing standards for poultry, as amended, applies; (g) food to which Council Regulation (EEC) No 1907/90 on certain marketing standards for eggs, as amended, applies.	f) & g) These European Council Regulations do not apply to catering.	Storage of shell eggs is not covered by these Regulations, but advice from the government's Chief Medical Officer is that caterers should store shell eggs in the fridge and use them by the 'Best Before' date.

Legal requirement	Guide to compliance	Advice on good practice

Reg. 6 (1) In any proceedings for an offence of contravening regulation 4(1), it shall be a defence for a person charged (for the purposes of this regulation called the 'defendant') to prove that -
(a) a food business responsible for manufacturing, preparing or processing the food has recommended that it is kept -
(i) at or below a specified temperature between 8°C and ambient temperatures, and
(ii) for a period not exceeding a specified shelf life;
(b) that recommendation has, unless the defendant is that food business, been communicated to the defendant either by means of a label on the packaging of the food or by means of some other appropriate form of written instruction;
(c) the food was not kept by the defendant at a temperature above the specified temperature; and
(d) at the time of the commission of the alleged offence, the specified shelf life had not been exceeded.
(2) A food business responsible for manufacturing, preparing or processing food shall not recommend that any food is kept -
(a) at or below a specified temperature between 8°C and ambient temperatures; and
(b) for a period not exceeding a specified shelf life,
unless that recommendation is supported by a well-founded scientific assessment of the safety of the food at the specified temperature.

Food described in Reg. 4 may be stored above 8°C if the producer can show that it is safe to do so. The producer must be able to demonstrate this scientifically as described below. (This provision will be of interest to producers of special food types who believe that temperatures below 8°C may affect the product quality. Caterers may use the provision, but are more likely to be interested in Reg. 7 which provides short term exemptions from 8°C for day to day practicalities.)

- If such food is prepared by the caterer -
- the caterer must establish a realistic safe storage life at the preferred storage temperature.
- the time/temperature for storage must be supported by a well founded scientific assessment* that food will be safe in those conditions.
- the caterer must ensure that the preferred storage temperature is not exceeded.
- the caterer must ensure that the food is used within the shelf life that has been established as safe.

- If such food is prepared by a manufacturer -
- the onus is on the manufacturer to make the scientific assessment*.
- the onus is on the manufacturer to pass on to the purchaser, who may be a caterer, the recommended storage temperature and the safe shelf life at that temperature.

Compliance by the caterer then involves:
- the caterer must keep the food at or below the recommended temperature.
- the caterer must use the product within the specified shelf life.

*It is unlikely that small businesses, including caterers, will have the expertise to do this scientific assessment themselves. Much more detailed guidance on the 'scientific assessment' is given in the guide to the England & Wales regulations from the Department of Health, London.

A food producer, including a caterer may decide that it would be preferable to keep food at a chilled temperature above 8°C.
- *because low temperature is detrimental to quality. For example pie crusts become less crisp.*
- *because 8°C provides a storage life longer than is needed in practice.*

Any caterer who chooses to make use of this provision should get specific expert advice. (Expert advice would be available from a food laboratory or consultant). A system of labelling will be advisable to ensure that food is used within the 'shelf life' established.

The caterer does not have to follow a suppliers recommendation to keep a food above 8°C. They may not have more than one chiller operating at different temperatures. They could simply choose to keep the food at normal chiller temperature.

Legal requirement	Guide to compliance	Advice on good practice

Reg. 7(1) In any proceedings for an offence of contravening regulation 4(1), it shall be a defence for a person charged to prove that the food-
(a) was for service or on display for sale;
(b) had not previously been kept for service or on display for sale at a temperature above 8°C or, in appropriate circumstances, the recommended temperature; and
(c) had been kept for service or on display for sale for a period of less than four hours.

Cold food may be kept above 8°C to accommodate certain practicalities.

During service or display it may be kept for up to 4 hours at a temperature above 8°C.

- Only ONE such period of display is allowed no matter how short. For example, if a dish of food is put on display for 1 hour at the end of a service period, it CANNOT have another 3 hours above 8°C at the next service.
- Food which remains uneaten at the end of a display period does NOT have to be discarded provided that it is still fit for consumption. It must be restored to a temperature of 8°C or cooler and then kept at that temperature until it can be used safely.

The burden of proof is on the caterer. The caterer must be able to demonstrate that the time limit is observed.

Some food displays will operate at ambient temperature. Other displays may have some refrigeration, but may not be able to achieve/operate at 8°C or cooler at all points.

Both situations can make use of this tolerance. Any display that does not keep food below 8°C must work to the '4 hour rule'.

Good management of food displays will be important.

The amount of food on display should be kept to a minimum consistent with the pattern of trade.

There can be no clear cut rule as to when food should be judged 'fit for consumption' after a period of display. If in doubt, food should be discarded.

Food that is to be kept after display should be returned to chill as quickly as possible.

Systems to demonstrate that time limits are observed may include labelling of dishes to indicate when they went onto display. If the food service period lasts for less than 4 hours, (for example workplace cafeteria service) that may be enough in itself to demonstrate compliance with the time limit.

Topping up of bulk displays of food should also be avoided. Food at the bottom of the bulk dish may remain accidentally on display for much longer than 4 hours if topping-up is allowed.

Food Safety (Temperature Control) Regulations 1995 - Guide to compliance by Caterers

Legal requirement

Reg. 7(2) In any proceedings for an offence of contravening regulation 4(1), it shall be a defence for the person charged to prove that the food-
(a) was being transferred -
(i) to a vehicle used for the purposes of the activities of a food business from, or
(ii) from a vehicle used for the purposes of the activities of a food business to, premises (which includes vehicles) at which the food was going to be kept at or at below 8°C or, in appropriate circumstances, the recommended temperature;
or
(b) was kept at a temperature above 8°C or, in appropriate circumstances, the recommended temperature for an unavoidable reason, such as-
(i) to accommodate the practicalities of handling during and after processing or preparation,
(ii) the defrosting of equipment, or
(iii) temporary breakdown of equipment,
and was kept at a temperature above 8°C or, in appropriate circumstances, the recommended temperature for a limited period only and that period was consistent with food safety.

Guide to compliance

The regulations allow for the fact that food may rise above 8°C for limited periods of time in unavoidable circumstances such as:
- transfers to or from vehicles
- during handling or preparation
- during defrost of equipment
- during temporary breakdown of equipment

The regulation does NOT put specific figures on the length of time allowed or how warm the food might become. This tolerance is allowed as a defence. The burden of proof will be on the caterer to show that:
- the food was unavoidably above 8°C for one of the reasons allowed
- that it was above 8°C for only a limited period
- that the break in temperature control was consistent with food safety.

The acceptable limits will obviously depend upon the combination of time and temperature. Under normal circumstances, a single period of up to two hours is unlikely to be questioned.

Advice on good practice

It is good practice to organise all transfers of food so that exposure to warm ambient temperatures is reduced and that rises in food temperature are kept to a minimum.
- *put deliveries away quickly*
- *move chilled food first, then frozen, then grocery*

If collecting food from a cash and carry warehouse, insulated bags or boxes should be used for chilled foods described in Reg. 4. They should be taken straight back to the catering outlet and put quickly into chilled storage.

To avoid equipment breakdown, planned maintenance is recommended.

Good management should ensure that such periods are as short as possible.

Legal requirement	Guide to compliance	Advice on good practice
Reg. 8 No person shall in the course of the activities of a food business keep any food which - *(a) has been cooked or reheated; (b) is for service or on display for sale; and (c) needs to be kept hot in order to control the growth of pathogenic micro-organisms or the formation of toxins, at or in food premises at a temperature below 63°C.*	Hot food must be kept at 63°C or hotter. This will apply to the same types of food described in regulation 4. Food must be kept at 63°C or hotter, whether: • it is in the kitchen awaiting service or dispatch • or in transit to a serving point, no matter how near or far • or actually on display in the serving area. Some tolerances or limited exemptions from this provision are allowed for practical handling reasons. These are given in 9(2) below.	Generally hot hold or display equipment is designed to hold food at or above 63°C, but is not capable of heating or cooking foods from cold.
Reg. 9(1) In any proceedings for an offence of contravening regulation 8, it shall be a defence for a person charged to prove that- (a) a well-founded scientific assessment of the safety of the food at temperatures below 63°C has concluded that there is no risk to health if, after cooking or reheating, the food is held for service or on display for sale- (i) at a holding temperature which is below 63°C, and (ii) for period not exceeding a specified period of time; and (b) at the time of the commission of the alleged offence, the food was held in a manner which is justified in the light of that scientific assessment.	Caterers may establish a holding time for hot food at a temperature cooler than 63°C which will present no risk to health. This will require a scientific assessment similar to that required by regulation 6. The caterer must: • have evidence of that assessment • show that the food was kept within the time & temperature limits of the assessment.	Any caterer intending to use this provision should seek specific expert advice. The more general 2 hour exemption in 9(2)is likely to be adequate for most situations.
Reg. 9(2) In any proceedings for an offence of ontravening regulation 8, it shall be a defence for a person charged to prove that the food- *(a) had been kept for service or on display for sale for a period of less than two hours; and* *(b) had not previously been kept for service or on display for sale by that person.*	Hot food may be held for one period of up to 2 hours at a temperature cooler than 63°C. The caterer must be able to show that: • the food was for service or on display for sale • it had not been kept for more than 2 hours • it had only had one such period • Food which remains uneaten at the end of a display period does NOT have to be discarded provided that it is still fit for consumption. It must be restored to a suitable temperature (below 8°C or above 63°C) and then kept at that temperature until it can be used safely. (The advice given in 7(1) will also apply here.) The burden of proof is on the caterer. The caterer must be able to demonstrate that the time limit is observed.	Note: rare beef or other rare meats will often be cooler than 63°C in the centre. When these are displayed, for example on a carvery, they will effectively make use of this provision even if the surface temperature is above 63°C. This provision may prove useful for egg based sauces such as Hollandaise which may be coagulated by temperatures above 63°C.

Food Safety (Temperature Control) Regulations 1995 - Guide to compliance by Caterers

Legal requirement	Guide to compliance	Advice on good practice

Reg. 10(1) Subject to paragraph (2), no person shall in the course of the activities of a food business keep foodstuffs which are -
(a) raw materials, ingredients, intermediate products or finished products; and
(b) likely to support the growth of pathogenic micro-organisms or the formation of toxins,
at temperatures which would result in a risk to health .

This is a general requirement to keep food at 'safe' temperatures. Regulations 4 to 9 detail some specific requirements for temperature controls. In most circumstances, food businesses complying with the specific requirement to keep food below 8°C will also be complying with this more general requirement. But there may be some situations where the general requirement covers a wider range of foods or implies a more stringent standard than Regulations 4 to 9 (for example sous vide products). This is explained in more detail in 10(3) below.

- It covers all types of food, raw materials, ingredients, intermediate products and finished products that will support the growth of food poisoning micro-organisms. Raw materials such as fresh meat and poultry must be kept at 'safe' temperatures, for example, they must be kept refrigerated.
- No temperature is specified in this regulation.
- The combination of time and temperature will be important.
- Limited periods outside of temperature control are permitted during preparation, display, service, storage or transport but it would be an offence to keep food out of temperature control for so long that it could become unsafe.
- Compliance with this regulation will be a matter of time and temperature. It will depend upon how long the food has been or will be exposed to any particular temperature.

It is good practice to set fridges at a target food temperature of 5°C to allow a margin of error below the legal standard. This is particularly true for cabinet fridges where there can be significant temperature rises during frequent door opening.

It is also good practice to keep all hot food at 63°C or hotter.

(2) Consistent with food safety, limited periods outside temperature control are permitted where necessary to accommodate the practicalities of handling during preparation, transport, storage, display and service of food.

Food for preparation should be brought out of chilled storage in small batches that can be processed quickly with little rise in temperature. (The acceptable time will depend upon a number of factors, notably the temperature of the preparation room and what other processing the food will have before it is served).

(3) A person may contravene paragraph (1) notwithstanding that he complies with the requirements of regulations 4 & 8, and in particular the keeping of perishable foodstuffs at above a maximum storage temperature recommended in any special storage conditions for them may be in contravention of paragraph (1) notwithstanding that they are kept at a temperature of 8°C or below.

There are some limited circumstances where a maximum temperature less than 8°C will apply.
The labelling of some foods may recommend specific storage temperatures cooler than 8°C. Where the lower temperature is necessary to food safety the caterer must keep the food at or below the temperature specified on the label.

In most cases the temperature on the label will only be necessary for the quality of the food or to prevent spoilage during its shelf life. In these cases, the recommended temperature will not be a legal requirement.

It will not always be obvious whether any on-pack storage instructions relate to safety or simply to food quality. As a guide, foods labelled with a 'Use By' date are more likely to require chilled storage to ensure their safety. It is good practice to pay particular regard to special storage conditions on the labels of foods marked with a 'Use By' date.

The food supplier may be able to provide clarification.

Legal requirement	Guide to compliance	Advice on good practice

Reg. 11 A food business responsible for cooling any food which must, by virtue of this Part, be kept at a temperature below ambient temperatures shall cool that food as quickly as possible following-
(a) the final heat processing stage; or
(b) if no heat process is applied, the final preparation stage,
to the temperature at which, by virtue of this Part, it must be kept.

This regulation applies to any type of food covered by regulation 4 or the general regulation 10.
- Food that has become hot during a cooking or reheating process
- or warm during a process of preparation as described in 7(2)

This food must be brought back to a satisfactory chill temperature as quickly as possible.
The satisfactory chill temperature may be:
- 8°C for foods covered by reg. 4
- a higher temperature established by the procedures in reg. 6

It is not implicit that a blast chiller must be used to comply with the regulation.
Food that has become hot should be moved to a cool place to allow initial cooling and then to a refrigerator. Food that has become warmed to kitchen temperatures during preparation etc. should be returned to chilled storage once preparation is finished.

Faster chilling (i.e. within 90 mins.) is recommended if the chilled food is to be kept for several days, for example in a 'Cook Chill' system.

This provision does not mean that a blast chiller must be used. But in any circumstances, it is good practice to cool hot food through the critical zone from 60°C to 10°C in less than 4 hours and then to store it under refrigeration, for example at 5°C or cooler.

Splitting food into relatively small pieces or batches will assist the rate of cooling.

Air blast chilling units should not be overloaded with hot food above their design capacity.

It is good practice to allow the movement of clean air over and around food containers during cooling.

Reg. 12 For the purposes of regulations 6(2) and 9(1), the presence of a scientific assessment of the safety of any food in a guide to good hygiene practice which has been-
(a) forwarded by the Secretary of State to the Commission pursuant to article 5.5 of the Directive, unless the Secretary of State has announced that the guide no longer complies with article 3 of the Directive; or
(b) developed in accordance with article 5.6 and 7 of the Directive and published in accordance with article 5.8 of the Directive,
shall, until the contrary is proved, be considered sufficient evidence that the scientific assessment in question is well-founded.

No such assessment is included in this guide because no general variation from the 8°C requirement is proposed for any catering product.

Legal requirement	Guide to compliance	Advice on good practice
Reg. 13(1) Subject to paragraph (2), no person shall keep food with respect to which any commercial operation is being carried out at or in food premises otherwise than	This regulation will apply to any food that may support the growth of food poisoning organisms within the 'shelf life' for which the food will be kept. The types of food that will be subject to the provision are indicated in the table that follows.	It is good practice to keep all perishable food in refrigeration at 5°C or cooler.
(a) in a refrigerator or refrigerating chamber or in a cool ventilated place; or	If COLD this food must be kept either in a refrigerator or a cool well ventilated place. No temperature is specified in law. The temperature deemed suitable will depend upon a number of factors including: • the type of food • how it has been prepared • what further preparation will take place • how long it will be held	
(b) at a temperature above 63°C.	If HOT this food must be kept at 63°C or hotter.	

Foods that are likely to be subject to Regulation 13(1)

Food Type	Comments
Cooked meats and fish, meat and fish products.	Includes prepared meals, meat pies, pâtés, potted meats, quiches and similar dishes based on fish.
Cooked meats in cans which have been pasteurised rather than fully sterilised.	Typically large catering packs of ham or cured shoulder.
Cooked vegetable dishes.	Includes cereals, rice & pulses.
Any cooked dish containing egg or cheese.	Includes flans, pastries etc.
Prepared salads and dressings.	Includes mayonnaise and prepared salads with mayonnaise or any other style of dressing. Some salads or dressings may have a formulation (especially the level of acidity**) that is adequate to prevent growth of pathogens.
Soft cheeses / mould ripened cheeses (after ripening).	Cheeses will include Camembert, Brie, Stilton, Roquefort, Danish Blue and any similar style of cheese.
Smoked or cured fish, and raw scombroid fish.	For example smoked salmon, smoked trout, smoked mackerel, etc. Also raw tuna, mackerel and other scombroid fish.
Any sandwiches whose fillings include any of these types of food.	
Low acid** desserts and cream products.	Includes dairy desserts, fromage frais and cream cakes. *Some artificial cream may be 'ambient stable' due to low water activity and/or high sugar and does not need to be kept in a cool place. It may be necessary to get clarification from suppliers.*
Fresh pasta and uncooked or partly cooked pasta and dough products.	Includes unbaked pies and sausage rolls, unbaked pizzas and fresh pasta.
Smoked or cured meats which are not ambient stable.	Salami, parma hams and other fermented meats will *not* be subject to temperature controls if they are ambient shelf stable.

Note (in box next to "Cooked vegetable dishes" / "Any cooked dish containing egg or cheese"): Some cooked vegetable or dessert recipes may have sufficiently high sugar content* (possibly combined with other factors like acidity) to prevent the growth of pathogenic bacteria. These will not be subject to mandatory temperature control.

* Technically, aW (water activity) is the key criterion.
**Technically, pH 4.5 (or more acid) is the critical limit. (See Glossary)

Legal requirement	Guide to compliance	Advice on good practice
Reg. 13(2) Paragraph (1) shall not apply to any food- *(a) which is undergoing preparation for sale;* *(b) which is exposed for sale or has been sold to a consumer whether for immediate consumption or otherwise;* *(c) which, immediately following any process of cooking to which it is subjected or the final processing stage if no cooking process is applied, is being cooled under hygienic conditions as quickly as possible to a temperature which would not result in a risk to health;* *(d) which, in order that it may be conveniently available for sale on the premises to consumers, it is reasonable to keep otherwise than as referred to in paragraph (1);* *(e) which, for the duration of its shelf life, may be kept at ambient temperatures with no risk to health;*	Food does NOT have to be kept cold or above 63°C in certain circumstances: • it is undergoing preparation for sale • it is exposed for sale or it has already been sold • it is being cooled. The cooling requirement is described in more detail under Reg. 16(3) • it is available to consumers for sale • it is shelf stable	
(f) to which Council Regulation (EEC) No 1906/90 on certain marketing standards for poultry, as amended, applies; *(g) to which Council Regulation (EEC) 1907/90 on certain marketing standards for eggs, as amended, applies;*	f) & g)These European Council Regulations do not apply to catering outlets.	Storage of shell eggs is not covered by these Regulations, but advice from the government's Chief Medical Officer is that caterers should store shell eggs in the fridge and use them by the 'Best Before' date.

Legal requirement	Guide to compliance	Advice on good practice
Reg. 14(1) Food which in the course of a commercial operation has been heated and which is thereafter re-heated before being served for immediate consumption or exposed for sale shall, on being reheated, be raised to a temperature of not less than 82°C.	In Scotland only, food that is being reheated must be raised to a temperature of 82°C or hotter. This provision applies only to food which has received its primary cooking in the same 'commercial operation', that is pre-cooked in the catering outlet or a central production unit belonging to the operation. It does not apply to food prepared by third parties, for example cook-frozen prepared foods.	*It is good practice to reheat dishes which have been commercially prepared by a third party to a core temperature of at least 70°C for 2 minutes or an absolute minimum of 75°C if no time is measured.*
Reg. 14(2) In any proceedings for an offence under para (1), it shall be a defence for the person charged to prove that he could not have raised the food to a temperature of not less than 82°C without a deterioration of its qualities.	82°C reheat does not have to be achieved if this is detrimental to food quality. The burden of proof is on the caterer, who must show that 82°C is detrimental. For example many cook-freeze and cook-chill dishes maybe adversely affected by 82°C reheat and may be exempt by virtue of this provision.	*It is good practice to reheat all dishes, including those which have been commercially prepared by a third party, to a core temperature of at least 70°C for 2 minutes or an absolute minimum of 75°C if no time is measured.*
Reg. 15 (1) Gelatine intended for use in the preparation of bakers' confectionery filling, meat products or fish products in the course of the activities of a food business shall, immediately before use, be brought to the boil or brought to and kept at a temperature of not less than 71°C for 30 minutes. (2) Any gelatine left over after the completion of the process shall, if not treated as waste, be cooled under hygienic conditions as quickly as is reasonably practicable and when cold shall be kept in a refrigerator or a refrigerating chamber or a cool ventilated place.	In Scotland only there are specific rules about the use of gelatine: 1. Immediately before use it must be boiled or held at 71°C or hotter for at least 30 minutes. 2. Left over gelatine must be discarded or cooled quickly and stored in a refrigerator or cool larder. (No temperature is specified). 3. Leftover gelatine must be pasteurised again before re-use, using either of the treatments described in 1.	*It would be good practice to keep gelatine in a fridge at 5°C or cooler and away from raw meat or other sources of contamination.*

Food Safety (Temperature Control) Regulations 1995 - Guide to compliance by Caterers

Legal requirement	Guide to compliance	Advice on good practice
Reg. 16(1) Subject to paragraphs (2) & (3), no person shall in the course of the activities of a food business keep any products which are - *(a) raw materials, ingredients, intermediate products or finished products; and* *(b) likely to support the growth of pathogenic micro-organisms or the formation of toxins,* *at temperatures which would result in a risk to health.*	This is a general requirement to keep food at 'safe' temperatures. Regulations 13 to 15 detail some specific requirements for food temperature controls in Scotland. In most circumstances food businesses complying with these specific requirements will also be complying with the general requirement. ● This provision covers all types of food, raw materials, ingredients, intermediate products and finished products that will support the growth of food poisoning micro-organisms. Raw materials such as fresh meat and poultry must be kept at 'safe' temperatures, for example, they must be kept in a refrigerator. ● No temperature is specified in this regulation. ● The combination of time and temperature will be important.	It is good practice to store all perishable food in effective chilled storage, usually at 5°C or cooler. It is also good practice to keep all hot food at 63°C or hotter.
16 (2) Consistent with food safety, limited periods outside temperature control are permitted where necessary to accommodate the practicalities of handling during preparation, transport, storage, display and service of food.	Limited periods outside of temperature control are permitted during preparation, display, service, storage or transport but it would be an offence to keep food out of temperature control for so long that it could become unsafe. Compliance with this provision will be a matter of time and temperature. It will depend upon how long the food has been or will be exposed to any particular temperature.	Food for preparation should be brought out of chilled storage in small batches that can be processed quickly with little rise in temperature. (The acceptable time will depend upon a number of factors, notably the temperature of the preparation room and what other processing the food will have before it is served). Holding times at warm temperatures below 63°C should also be kept to a minimum.

Legal requirement	Guide to compliance	Advice on good practice

Reg. 16(3) Paragraph (1) shall not apply to any food which immediately following a final heat processing stage, or a final preparation stage if no heat process is applied, is being cooled as quickly as possible to a temperature which would not result in a risk to health.

This requirement applies to the same types of food described previously in Reg. 16(1).

- Food that has become hot during a cooking or reheating process
- or warm by a break in the 'cold chain' during preparation

This food must be brought back to a satisfactory chill temperature as quickly as possible.

It is not implicit that a blast chiller must be used to comply with the regulation.

Food that has become hot should be moved to a cool place to allow initial cooling and then to a refrigerator.

Food that has become warm during preparation etc. should be returned to chilled storage once preparation is finished.

Faster chilling (i.e. within 90 mins) is recommended if the chilled food is to be kept for several days, for example in a 'Cook Chill' system.

This provision does not mean that a blast chiller must be used. But in any circumstances, it is good practice to cool hot food through the critical zone from 60°C to 10°C in less than 4 hours and then to store it under refrigeration, for example at 5°C or cooler.

Splitting food into relatively small pieces or batches will assist the rate of cooling.

Air blast chillers should not be overloaded with hot food above their design capacity.

It is good to allow the movement of clean air over and around food containers during cooling.

Food Safety (Temperature Control) Regulations 1995 - Guide to compliance by Caterers

Annex

PRACTICAL TEMPERATURE CONTROL OF FOOD IN CATERING PREMISES

Section 1
Introduction

This Annex to the guidelines provides practical advice on temperature control. *It is not part of the guide to compliance.* It describes the characteristics of various types of chill and hot holding equipment commonly used by caterers. It also suggests methods of temperature monitoring that may be used for each.

Summary

The temperatures in refrigerated and hot holding equipment will often be variable.

Temperature can vary from point to point within the unit. From front to back; from top to bottom; and from side to side. The variation will differ from unit to unit depending upon the pattern of air circulation and its efficiency. Units with fans should show less variation than those without.

Temperature can vary during the working day. During busy periods after frequent door opening, the temperature will tend to rise. There will also be a rise during defrost cycles.

The temperature may also vary over a longer time period. For example, fridge units will often be less efficient on hot days, or the compressor fan may gradually block up with dust. A unit working well today may not be efficient in a month's time.

For these reasons:
1. Regular checks are necessary to show that temperatures stay within the legal standards.
2. These checks must be done carefully to make sure that the temperature measured is a good reflection of the temperature of food held in the unit. In some circumstances you will need to take temperatures at more than one spot.

Various types of temperature controlled equipment used in catering outlets are described in the following sections. They can only be used and monitored properly when operators are aware of their characteristics. This Part of the guidelines provides practical advice on these issues.

Monitoring

The guidelines describe many different types of chilled storage and display equipment, but three basic principles of monitoring are applied to all of them:

1. Locate the warmest (and maybe the coldest) part of the unit. Always check temperatures at the warmest point. ('Worst case')

2. Air temperatures will fluctuate much faster than food especially as doors are opened and closed. A 'damped' sensor response gives a more reliable reading.

3. The law relates to food temperatures. In many cases it is more convenient to measure air temperatures in the unit. The two may not always be the same. A 'load test' will establish the relationship between air temperature readings and that of the food.

In some situations air temperature measurement is quite unreliable, for example open display units with minimal or no air circulation and hot holding units. Food temperatures are the only reliable method of monitoring.

Good practice

Chilling or hot holding equipment will only work effectively if they are properly installed and managed and maintained.

1.1 Regular maintenance and cleaning

On fridge units pay special attention to cleaning air intakes, air outlets, the fins or grills of evaporators, defrost water drainage channels and door seals.

If the unit is fitted with a temperature display, check it periodically to make sure that the readout is reliable and accurate. Accuracy can be checked against a calibrated hand held probe.

1.2 Siting

The position of chill units may effect their efficiency. Beware:
- High temperatures in the surrounding room or kitchen
- Restricted air flow to compressors
- Draughts, especially across open display units
- Warm air from nearby heaters or cooking equipment
- Radiant energy including sunlight or lamps falling directly onto or into units

(For many fridge installations, different standards of compressor unit can be specified. In many catering outlets, fridge units will be working in warm ambient conditions and it is recommended that higher specification units are chosen, that is compressors designed to operate at around 45°C.)

1.3 Management

Chill display and holding units do not reduce food temperatures efficiently. Food should already be cooled before it is put on display. Even the food containers may have a significant effect on food temperature, especially heavy ones such as ceramic bowls. Ideally, containers should also be pre-cooled.

During preparation, for example sandwich preparation, take the ingredients from chilled storage in small batches that can be used quickly and return the finished product to chill as quickly as possible.

The same applies to hot holding equipment. It should only be loaded with food that is already properly heated or cooked, for example the glass fronted display units typically used for pies are unsuitable for actually warming the pies.

1.4 Air circulation and loading

Proper air circulation is vital for effective temperature control in all types of equipment.
- The basic design of the unit is important. But even the best designs are likely to have warmer spots and cooler spots. In poorly designed units, the variation from coolest to warmest point can be very significant. These can be identified by temperature checks at different points in the load space, preferably using a logger.
- Don't load food into open display units so that it protrudes above the chilled air stream.

(This will sometimes be indicated by a 'load line'.)

- Don't overload units with too much food or by using containers that are unnecessarily large.
- Don't position food so that it blocks the air flow.

1.5 Containers

Containers that are good thermal insulators will interfere with the cooling effect. This can be a particular problem with direct contact units (dole plate or crushed ice). The problem is worse if the food itself is a good insulator, for example sandwiches made with thick bread.

1.6 Probe thermometers

Care must be taken that probes don't cause contamination.

- Make sure that they are kept clean and disinfected.
- Ideally don't use the same probe for highly contaminated food (for example, raw poultry) and ready to eat foods. If you must use the same probe make sure that it is properly cleaned and disinfected after use with raw food and before use with ready to eat foods. (Direct probing of food can be avoided by using 'damped' air probes or thermal simulants. These are both mentioned again later.)

1.7 Taking temperature readings

This can be done in a number of ways.

- *Taking air temperatures -* a hand held probe or a sensor fitted in the fridge or hot holding unit senses the air temperature. Points to note:
  - Air temperature may not be the same as food temperature (see 'load tests').
  - Air temperatures may vary. Be careful not to take a reading when the unit is on defrost cycle or when the door of the unit has just been opened. In some units, the temperature will be different at different points. A reading at just one point may be misleading.
- *Taking food temperatures -* the probe is inserted into the food. Points to note:
  - The food may not be the same temperature throughout, especially if it is still cooling down or warming up.
  - Probing may contaminate the food. (See 1.6 above)
  - Probing may puncture the food packing. It is not wise to do this in some instances, (for examples vac-packs). The food requires intact packaging to achieve its shelf life.
  - Because of the latter two points, this is sometimes referred to as 'destructive testing'.
- *'Between pack' test -* to overcome the problem of puncturing packaging, a good estimate of food temperature will come from a 'between pack' test. The probe is sandwiched between two packs. Special flat probes can be used. This method will be less accurate than direct food probing, a tolerance of about 2°C should be allowed.
- *Damped sensors or simulants -* help to overcome the problems of air temperature fluctuations. The probe or the simulant material is designed to respond only slowly to fluctuations.

Each type of testing has advantages and disadvantages and each will be more suited to a particular situation. The most suitable for any particular application will be outlined in the following guidance. Whenever probes are used, enough time should be allowed for the probe temperature to stabilise.

1.8 Temperature Records

There is no specific requirement to keep records of temperature checks. But records may be helpful to show that the legal requirements have been met. Equally, if any action is taken against a business under the Food Safety Act 1990 (or Regulations made under it), records may help the business to establish a 'due diligence' defence.

Any records should also make a note of action taken to remedy any discrepancies identified by routine monitoring.

FIGURE 2.0   WALK-IN CHILL STORE

FIGURE 2.1   AIR TEMPERATURE RECORD OF
                    A WALK-IN CHILL STORE

Section 2
Chilled Storage

2.1 Introduction
Chilled stores will be either walk-in units or 'reach-in' cabinet fridges. Walk-in units will usually have forced air circulation, that is the cold air will be circulated by a fan. Reach-in cabinets should also have forced air cooling, but some smaller units (domestic fridges) will only have a cooling plate or ice box.

More modern units may have display thermometers or even recorders. These may be used for temperature monitoring provided that they are accurate and the sensors are in appropriate positions. (Neither should be taken for granted). Tests which may be used to check this are described later.

If a unit is *not* fitted with a thermometer, you could monitor it using a hand held probe by checking either the air temperature or food temperatures. Both approaches need care. In storage units it is more usual to check the air temperature, but it will be important to check how this relates to the temperature of food in the unit by using a 'Load Test'.

Door opening can cause a big rise in the air temperature of chilled stores as cold air escapes to be replaced by warmer air. Smaller units are affected more than larger ones. Recovery can be slow. So checking the air temperature soon after door opening may not give an accurate picture of the operating efficiency of the fridge. (The point is illustrated graphically in Figs. 2.1, 2.5, and 2.6).

2.2 Walk-in Chill Stores
A diagram of a typical walk-in store is shown in Figure 2.0. Warmest and coolest locations in the store will depend upon the design, especially the position of the cooling unit and the door. A plastic strip curtain on the door is very useful to prevent the escape of cold air when the door is open.

2.2.1 Air Temperatures
Most walk-in units in catering premises will be relatively small, (below 500 cubic metres). One sensor should be enough to monitor the air temperature of the unit. The sensor should be placed at the warmest location in the store. This is likely to be in the air return to the cooling unit or on the wall opposite the cooling unit and just above the top shelf. (Both marked on Fig. 2.0). If the cooler unit is near the door, then the latter position is recommended.

A broader picture of the operating temperature will come from a second sensor fitted at the coldest spot, normally in the air coming off the cooling unit ('air off' temperature).

Air temperatures will fluctuate much more quickly than food temperatures, especially when the door is opened and the unit is in constant use. A sensor/readout that responds quickly to changes in air temperature is not necessary, in fact the readouts may be misleading. It is often better to have a sensor designed to respond more slowly, known as a 'damped sensor'.

A slower response can be achieved by embedding the probe into plastic or metal or immersing it in liquid (glycerol, oil or even water). In some systems the response is damped electronically.

A   (Air Off)
B   Return Air (Air On)
C   Load Limit or Warmest Point

FIGURE 2.4

Backplate
Gravity Feed

FIGURE 2.3

Ice Box
Gravity Feed

FIGURE 2.2

Forced Air

Practical Temperature Control

Damping is designed to prevent the sensor from responding to changes in temperature much faster than the food. It is equally important that the damping does not make the sensor respond more slowly than the food. A response time of 10-15 minutes is recommended for most applications.

(Some more sophisticated systems will try to mimic the food response more precisely. These systems are known as 'thermal simulants'. More information is given in a manual from the Campden & Chorleywood Food Research Association, see references. Suppliers of fridge equipment or thermometers may be able to provide more information.)

2.2.2 Recording Air Temperatures
The monitoring system will be most useful if the sensor is linked to an automatic recorder. Chart recorders have been used for many years. More recently data loggers have been introduced. Automatic alarms linked to the sensor can also provide useful safeguards.

Figure 2.1 is an example of a temperature record from a walk-in store. In this case, the sensor response was not damped.

If a recorder is not fitted, the sensor will be linked to a dial or digital readout. A routine should be established for checking temperatures and acting on discrepancies, and a record of the readings should be kept as a matter of good practice.

2.2.3 Load Test
Usually the actual temperature of the food will not be exactly the same as the air temperatures measured. A 'load test' helps you to understand the relationship. Provided the chilled unit has good air circulation, establishing the relationship is quite simple. The unit should be loaded with a typical load of chilled food and left for long enough to equalise with the chiller temperature. Food at a number of points in the store should be probed (either directly or 'between packs') and monitored frequently, preferably continuously using a logger. The monitoring period should be long enough to represent normal operating conditions. The air temperature should be monitored at the sensor point recommended in this guide over the same period. Comparing the two sets of readings establishes the relationship between air and food temperatures in that unit.

For any unit, a load test may only need to be done once to establish the relationship. Although it may be repeated occasionally to check that the relationship is still the same. In units which have less effective air circulation, a load test will not give such a reliable relationship. This includes equipment such as open display units or hot holding, so it is unwise to monitor these units by single point air temperature measurements. More advice is given later.

2.3 Cabinet Fridges ('reach in')
2.3.1 Fan assisted units
Figure 2.2 shows the diagram of a typical forced air storage chiller. In modern cabinets, the air flow is carefully channelled. Cold air is blown into the base of the unit and passes up through the storage space to return to the fan and over the cooler unit from the top of the storage space. Coolest points will normally be at the base of the unit and warmest at the top especially above the fan intake where cooling is at a minimum (point C in the figure).

In older units, the air may not be blown over the cooling unit (evaporator), the fan simply mixes the air in the cabinet. These are obviously much less efficient.

2.3.1.1 Temperature monitoring
Systems will normally be based on air temperature monitoring similar to those described in 2.2. Because door opening is likely to cause bigger fluctuations in smaller cabinets, 'damping' of the sensor response becomes even more important. The effect of damping is shown in Fig. 2.6.

One sensor will normally be fitted. It should be positioned as close as possible to the 'air return' grill.

Ideally sensors will be linked to a recording device (chart or data logger). The on-cost may be more difficult to justify on a cabinet fridge than it is on a larger walk-in, although costs of loggers have fallen significantly over the last few years.

Alternatively, sensors will be linked to a dial or digital display and these should be checked routinely (see 2.2.2). To get an accurate picture of the holding temperature achieved by the unit, it would be good practice to check it at least twice a day, and that should include at least one check during or straight after a busy period of use.

2.3.2 'Static' Air Cabinets

These units do not have blown air circulated by a fan. They rely upon air circulating slowly by natural convection currents which is slow and unreliable. Temperature variations even within a small storage space may be even greater than in large walk-in units. The temperature will change significantly with door openings and will take longer to recover. ***These units are effectively domestic equipment and may not be capable of keeping food at the temperatures required by law in a food business.***

There are basically two designs and the temperature distribution can be quite different.

Ice Box Coolers. These older models had a small ice box at the top of the storage space. A typical design is shown in Fig. 2.3. Coolest parts are immediately under the ice box, either the top or middle shelves.

Back Plate Coolers. These cabinets are cooled by a plate evaporator fitted to or just behind the back wall of the storage space. Fig. 2.4 is a typical design. The cold air falls from the plate at the back of the storage space and coolest parts of the unit will be the rear of the lower shelves. Warmes spots will be at the front of the top shelf. There is very little cooling effect above the level of the back plate on the top shelf. The advantage of the backplate design is that it allows automatic defrost to be included.

2.3.2.1 Temperature Monitoring

Both designs are inefficient and recover temperature only very slowly, so meaningful monitoring is difficult especially if it is based on air temperature checks. A 'damped' sensor would be essential and monitoring should try to focus on the warmest location in the unit.

Temperatures should be monitored regularly as described above and a periodic 'load test' would be needed to validate the relationship between the temperature checks and the temperature of the food at various points in the unit.

FIGURE 2.5
AIR TEMPERATURE RECORD OF A FAN ASSISTED CABINET

FIGURE 2.6   **EXAMPLE OF A "DAMPED" SENSOR**

Section 3
Chilled Display Units

3.1 Introduction
Chilled display units may be:
- closed (cabinets with doors)
- open (self service)
- semi-enclosed (food is served over by a catering assistant)

Cooling systems may rely on a number of principles:
- forced air - cool air is circulated by a fan
- gravity ('tumble' or 'cascade')- cool air falls by natural convection
- conduction through direct contact - dole plate or crushed ice units
- a combination of conduction with one of the other two

In principle, forced air units should be the more effective, but many designs are inefficient. Static systems may have even greater temperature variations across the load space and will be more difficult to monitor. With direct contact units, the measurement of air temperatures is futile.

It can be very difficult consistently to achieve temperatures of 8°C or cooler in chilled display units. If the caterer intends to display food (of the type covered by the regulations) for more than 4 hours, he should be certain that the equipment can hold it at 8°C or cooler. If the unit cannot achieve this, then the caterer will need to apply the '4 hour rule' which is described in Part 5 Section 1 of this guide.

3.2 Closed Display units
Closed display units will include multi-deck cabinets used to display sandwiches, drinks and other foods. Multi-deck units fitted with plastic strip curtains are effectively in this category. A typical design is shown in Fig. 3.0.

Unlike storage cabinets, cooling units tend to be in the base and cold air enters the cabinet from the top and back. Warmest locations will tend to be at the front of the lowest shelf. On wide shelves, the outer extremes of the shelf tend to be cooler than the centre. If the unit has a glass door, radiant heat may also affect food at the front of the shelf.

Frequent door opening is likely at busy trading periods and it is important that food is properly pre-cooled before it is loaded into display units.

3.2.1 Temperature Monitoring
Similar systems to 'reach in' storage cabinets will apply e.g. air temperature monitoring, using a 'damped' sensor located at the warmest spot in the unit and linked ideally to a recorder, or to a dial or digital readout. The location of the warmest part of the unit will be different to a 'reach in' cabinet, the differences are described above. A second sensor at the coolest spot may also be used to give a more complete picture.

"AIR-OFF"

"AIR-ON"

FIGURE 3.0   **GLASS DOORED DISPLAY CABINET**

AMBIENT

"AIR-OFF"

REFRIGERATED
AREA

Health safety
cut-out position
(or where
specified by the
manufacturer)

"AIR-ON"

MACHINE FRONT ELEVATION

MACHINE SIDE ELEVATION

FIGURE 3.1   **VENDING MACHINE**

3.3 Vending Machines

Refrigerated vending machines are usually very similar in design to the cabinet displays described in the previous section. Air flow patterns tend to be similar and are illustrated in Fig. 3.1. Access doors tend to be smaller in vending machines, so the effects of door opening on the operating temperature will not be so severe.

Operating a vending machine within the '4 hour rule' would not be practical and it is important that it is capable of achieving temperatures of 8°C or cooler if it is used to display food that is covered by the regulations.

3.3.1 Temperature Monitoring

Vending machines are frequently used in situations, sometimes remote, where they receive minimal attention from the operator. The fitting of automatic recording systems is particularly helpful but a direct digital readout on the unit is also useful. The principles from 3.2 will apply to choosing the type of sensor and its location. As an added safeguard, many machines are also fitted with a thermal cut-out. The machine is inactivated and food cannot be vended again until it has received attention.

3.4 Open/Semi-open Display units

Open display units are the type most commonly used in catering operations. They will be used for a wide variety of applications, breakfast buffets, starters and hors d'ouvres, sandwiches, salads, desserts, etc. Designs may be completely open; have small screens (euphemistically referred to as 'sneeze screens'), or be semi-enclosed. In the last case, food is either served over the unit from the open back by a catering assistant or self served through hinged flaps.

Semi-open designs are likely to have more even temperatures than open units but there is a huge variation in individual designs.

Food temperature will depend upon a number of factors including:
- its temperature before it is put on display
- the design and efficiency of the display unit
- the containers used
- how food is arranged in the load space
- the temperature of the surrounding room or area

3.4.1 Forced Air Units & 'Natural Convection' (tumble air) Units

In the former almost invariably cold air is blown from grills at the rear of the display and returns to the evaporator through grills at the front. (Fig. 3.2.b).

Natural convection units cool ambient (warm) air which tumbles across the load space by gravity; there is effectively no 'air return'. Temperature control is much less focused in this type of unit and they are less efficient.

In both types of unit, a well of cool air is created in the load space. It is important that food is not stacked so high that it is above the height of this well. Some units have a 'load line' to indicate this. This is illustrated by Fig. 3.4 which shows a temperature of 1.5°C at 102mm above the base, but as high as 5°C only 50mm higher at the same place in the load space.

A comprehensive load test would be vital to identify the characteristics of any open display unit and to help to identify suitable monitoring points. (Warmest/coolest). The load test should remember to check different heights above the deck as well as left/right and front/back dimensions.

3.4.1.1 Temperature Monitoring

Air temperature checks must be treated with special caution in this type of unit. They may be more reliable in forced air units but systems should not rely upon a single sensor at the 'air off' position. Much better is to have sensors at both 'air off' and 'air return' but even then they will only provide some guide to the operating efficiency of the unit. They will not indicate the actual temperature of the food on display.

Food simulants at one or more locations in the display deck may provide a more reliable solution. Care will need to be taken in choosing a simulant appropriate to the food in the unit, as well as in choosing its position.

3.4.2 Conduction Cooling Units (Dole Plate or Crushed Ice Displays)

The units conduct heat away from the base of the food through contact with a cold base plate or bed of ice. They rely almost entirely upon direct contact (see Fig 3.3). This is a fairly inefficient system of heat transfer at best and it can easily be impeded, for example:

- if the food container is a poor conductor of heat
- if there is poor contact with the base plate or ice. For example if food is lifted above it by plastic matting, an inverted plate, etc. Tall narrow containers give very limited contact area, wide low ones (plates) are much more suitable
- if the food itself is a poor conductor of heat. A large bowl of rice salad may be cold at the base, but heat will not be taken from the upper layers. In some cases the food is composite, for example it is the cream of a cream cake that needs to be kept refrigerated, but it will be separated from the dole plate by a layer of cake which does not conduct heat.

Warm air from the surrounding room will also have a significant effect on the food temperature.

3.4.2.1 Temperature Monitoring

Monitoring of air temperatures in this type of unit serves no useful purpose. Even food simulants have very limited value. Direct measurement of food temperatures will provide a better indication.

3.5 Cool Boxes, Insulated Boxes & Trolleys, and Eutectic plates

Transport of chilled foods can take place in insulated boxes or trolleys with eutectic plates or gel packs. Any system of this type is designed to maintain the temperature of food for only a limited period of time. These systems will not cool food down; it should already be pre-cooled. Taking lids on and off or opening doors will allow warm air to enter and recovery of temperature will be very slow.

The simplest method of temperature monitoring is to check food temperature before it is loaded into boxes or trolleys and then again when it is unloaded. It may be good practice to keep a record of these temperatures.

EVAPORATOR

"AIR-OFF"

VERTICAL SCREEN

a) CASCADE

"AIR-ON"

"AIR-OFF"

"AIR OFF"

"AIR-ON"

VERTICAL SCREEN

EVAPORATOR

b) FORCED AIR CIRCULATION

FIGURE 3.2   **CHILLED OPEN DISPLAY UNIT**

COILED TANK

FIGURE 3.3   **DOLE WELL**

84

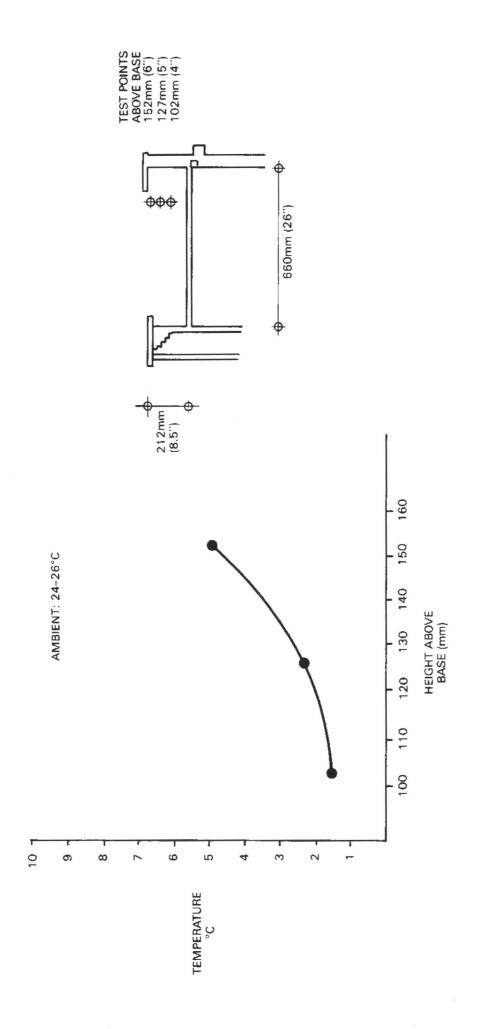

TEST POINTS
ABOVE BASE
152mm (6")
127mm (5")
102mm (4")

660mm (26")

212mm
(8.5")

AMBIENT: 24–26°C

TEMPERATURE
°C

10
9
8
7
6
5
4
3
2
1

100 110 120 130 140 150 160

HEIGHT ABOVE
BASE (mm)

**AIR TEMPERATURES AT DIFFERENT HEIGHTS
IN A SERVE-OVER CABINET**

FIGURE 3.4

Section 4
Hot Food Holding & Display

4.1 Introduction

There are several different types of hot holding or display equipment including the following:

- Hot cupboards and cabinets including meat pie displays
- Bains marie using wet, dry, or vapour systems (Fig 4.0)
- Hot plates and heated servery display tops (Fig. 4.1)
- Carvery units with bottom and/or top heat
- 'Burger chutes'

Hot cupboards and cabinets usually have one or more heated surfaces inside a closed unit with doors. Heat is transferred to the food by hot air convection.

'Bains marie' are designed for use with modular containers which are surrounded by hot water, steam, or hot air. Transfer of heat through solid food relies upon conduction and is slow. Lids should be kept on containers whenever possible to prevent heat loss.

Hot plates and heated servery tops provide a hot display surface. Transfer of heat to the food is by conduction through the base of the dish, therefore the temperature of the food is lower the further away from the source of heating.

The use of overhead heaters prolongs the holding time, and they are often used in conjunction with base heating to keep the surface of the food hot e.g. for open dishes in servery heated tops. There are many overhead heaters available. Most employ infra-red lamps to heat the food and many have the additional advantage of light to illuminate the display area.

As with refrigerated displays, the hot holding equipment is only designed to maintain food already heated or cooked to the correct temperature. It is important that food is above 63°C just before being placed in the holding equipment, and storage time is kept to a minimum.

If hot food (of the type subject to the Regulations) is to be held for more than 2 hours, the equipment must achieve 63°C or hotter. If it cannot achieve this temperature, the '2 hour' rule will apply (Regulation 9(2) in Part 5 Section 1 of this guide.)

4.2 Temperature monitoring

Hot cupboards and cabinets are particularly susceptible to large fluctuations of temperature when doors are opened to load or remove food. Therefore, the taking of air temperatures with a probe to monitor these units is not recommended. Hot cupboard thermostats/thermometers should only be regarded as guides to internal temperatures, as variations will be found throughout the cupboard space. A 'damped' sensor (as described in 2.2.1) may give more useful information by reducing the air temperature fluctuations, provided that it is located in the coolest part. Also, it needs to be related to food temperature provided they have been loaded in the correct temperature range.

Temperature readings of bains maries and heated top surfaces will usually bear little relation to the displayed food temperature, and are only recommended as evidence that the equipment is working.

Temperatures of displayed and stored food will vary in relation to the source of heat, and there may be differences from surface to centre of the food. Therefore, regular monitoring is best accomplished by temperature measurements with a probe on several food products at different points in the equipment.

OVERHEAD HEATER

MODULAR CONTAINER

HEATING MEDIUM

FIGURE 4.0   **BAINS MARIE**

OVERHEAD HEATER

FIGURE 4.1   **HEATED BASE AND HOT LAMP**

Section 5
Temperature Measuring Equipment

Various designs of thermometer are available.

1. Electronic probe thermometers
A solid metal probe has a temperature sensor located at its tip and is linked to the electronic unit which includes a digital display.

These probes can be used for both hot and cold temperatures and a variety of applications:
- Air temperatures in fridges or freezers
- Food temperatures in fridges, hot cupboards or on display
- Checking internal food temperatures during cooling, cooking, or reheating
- Checking the temperature of food deliveries

Specification
Environmental Health Officers have been advised to use instruments with a high specification, e.g. :
- Accuracy of +/-0.5°C or better (in the range 0°C to 20°C)
- Accuracy must not be significantly affected by changing ambient temperatures, i.e. must not changed by more than 0.3°C across the ambient range 0°C to 30°C
- Display must be readable to 0.1°C intervals or less
- System should reach 90% of its final reading within 3 minutes
- The system should be robust and shockproof
- The probe should be designed to promote good thermal contact

Probes used by caterers do not necessarily need such a high specification. In choosing an instrument, key qualities will be
- Speed of response
- Accuracy
- Cleanability

The two parts of the unit need to be checked for accuracy.
The electronic display unit should be checked at least once per year. Manufacturers may offer a service or 'calibration caps' that plug into the unit may be used.

The probe and system together can be checked monthly by using simple procedures:

- *Cold* - agitate the probe in a mixture of ice and a small amount of water until a steady reading is achieved. This should be -1°C to +1°C. If outside this range, the unit should be repaired.
- *Hot* - agitate the probe in boiling unsalted water until a steady reading is achieved. This should be between 99°C and 101°C. If outside this range, the unit should be repaired.

2. Liquid crystal thermometers

These cheap plastic strip thermometers can be useful in storage units that do not have any other type of thermometer built in. They must be read 'in situ' because their reading will change quickly if they are taken out of the unit. Sticking them to the door or wall of the unit will 'damp' their response.

3. Glass thermometers

These thermometers pose a serious risk of contamination when used in a food environment, both from broken glass and from mercury. Their use is not recommended. On no account should food be probed with a glass thermometer.

Part 6 Glossary, references & contacts

References

Assured Safe Catering
Department of Health. ISBN 0 11 321688 2 Price £8.50
From The Stationery Office PO Box 276, London, SW8 5DT Tel. 0171 873 9090

Assured Safe Catering
Free summary leaflet from: Department of Health Distribution Centre PO Box 410, Wetherby LS23 7LN

Council Directive on the Hygiene of foodstuffs . EC93/43/EEC
Official Journal of the European Communities, No. L 175/1 18 July 1993.
[From The Stationery Office, PO Box 276, London, SW8 5DT Tel. 0171 873 9090]

S.A.F.E. [Systematic Assessment of Food Environment]
Available from British Hospitality Association, Queens House,
55–56 Lincoln's Inn Fields, London WC2A 3BH
Tel 0171 404 7744 Fax 0171 404 7799 Price £5.50

Industry Guides: A Template
Department of Health, Distribution Centre, PO Box 410, Wetherby LS23 7LN.

Food Labelling Regulations 1996
SI No. 1499 from The Stationery Office

Food Safety Act 1990
from The Stationery Office

Food Safety (General Food Hygiene) Regulations 1995
SI No. 1763 from The Stationery Office

Food Safety (Temperature Control) Regulations 1995
SI No. 2200 from The Stationery Office

Growth of Cl. perfringens in cooked chili during cooling. Applied & Env. Micro. May 1988 p1104-1108
Blankenship et al.

Guidance on the Food Safety (Temperature Control) Regulations 1995
Department of Health, Room 501A, Skipton House, 80 London Road, London SE1 6LW

A Guide to the General Temperature Control Regulations
Department of Health, Distribution Centre, PO Box 410, Wetherby, LS23 7LN

A Guide to the General Food Hygiene Regulations
Department of Health, Distribution Centre, PO Box 410, Wetherby, LS23 7LN

A Guide to Food Hazards And Your Business
Department of Health, Distribution Centre, PO Box 410, Wetherby, LS23 7LN

Guidelines for the use of Thermal Simulation Systems in the chilled food industry.
Campden & Chorleywood Food RA, Chipping Campden, Gloucestershire GL55 6LD

Influence of Heating and cooling rates on spore germination and growth of Cl perfringens in media and in roast beef.Jpn J Vet Sci 47(2): 259-267 1985
Shigehisa et al

References

A list of Codes of Practice applicable to foods
Institute of Food Science and Technology ISBN 0 905 367 12X £35

Private Water Supplies Regulations 1991
SI 1991 2790 ISBN 0 11 015872 5 from The Stationery Office

Private Water Supplies (Scotland) Regulations 1992 ISBN 0 11 023575 4 from The
The Stationery Office

Supply of Machinery (Safety) Regulations 1992
SI No. 1992 3073 ISBN 0 11 025719 7 from The Stationery Office

Workplace (Health Safety & Welfare) Regulations 1992 ISBN 0 11 886332 9
The Stationery Office

Food Handlers – Fitness to Work
Department of Health £2.50
Department of Health Distribution Centre, PO Box 410, Wetherby LS23 7LN

Water Bye-laws 1989
Available from regional water supply companies.

Contacts

Chartered Institute of Environmental Health
Chadwick Court, 15 Hatfields, London, SE1 8DJ
Tel: 0171 928 6006 Fax: 0171 261 1960

Joint Hospitality Industry Congress
c/o British Hospitality Association, Queens House, 55–56 Lincoln's Inn
Fields, London WC2A 3BH Tel: 0171 404 7744 Fax 0171 404 7799

LACOTS (Local Authorities Co-ordinating Body on Food and Trading Standards)
PO Box 6, 1A Robert St., Croydon, CR9 1LG
Tel: 0181 688 1996 Fax: 0181 680 1509

Mobile and Outdoor Caterers Association of Great Britain (MOCA)
Centre Court, 1301 Stratford Road, Hall Green,
Birmingham, B28 9AP Tel: 0121 693 7000 Fax 0121 693 7100

Royal Environmental Health Institute of Scotland
3 Manor Place, Edinburgh, EH3 7DH Tel: 0131 225 6999 Fax. 0131 225 3993

Royal Institute of Public Health and Hygiene
28 Portland Place, London, W1N 4ED Tel: 0171 580 2731

Royal Society of Health
38A St George's Drive, London, SW1V 4BH Tel: 0171 630 0121

Society of Food Hygiene Technology
PO Box 37, Lymington, Hants, SO41 9WL Tel/Fax: 01590 671979

Institute of Food Science and Technology (IFST)
5 Cambridge Court, 210 Shepherds Bush Rd., London, W6 7NJ
Tel: 0171 603 6316 Fax: 0171 602 9936

The Stationery Office
PO Box 276, London SW8 5DT Tel: 0171 873 9090

Department of Health
Department of Health, Room 501A, Skipton House, 80 London Road, London
SE1 6LW Tel: 0171 972 5071 Fax: 0171 972 5141

Glossary	
Acidity/low acid	Pickling or fermentation will increase the acidity of food and act as a preservative. Some foods are naturally higher in acid (e.g. fruits). Levels of pH below 4.5 will prevent the growth of pathogenic bacteria. Low acid foods will have less acid, and therefore a 'higher' pH. (See 'pH')
Aerosols	Airborne contamination.
'Air-off'	The flow of air leaving the cooling unit of a fridge system. It will be at its coolest at this point.
'Air-on'	The flow of air returning to the cooling unit of a fridge system. It will be at its warmest at this point.
Ambient temperature	The temperature of the surrounding environment. Commonly used to mean room temperature.
Antiseptic rub	Liquid applied after hand washing and drying to further reduce levels of contamination on hands. Especially useful before handling 'high risk' foods.
aW	Water activity. A measure of the water available in a food to support microbiological growth. 'High aW' foods will support the growth of bacterial pathogens, 'Low aW' foods will be preserved. aW is not the same as water content. Some foods with high water content have relatively low aW because the water is bound up with dissolved salts or sugar. For example jam has high water content but relatively low aW.
Bacteria	A group of single cell living organisms. Some may spoil food and some may actually cause illness.
Bactericidal detergent	Detergents used either for handwash or equipment cleaning that not only remove dirt but also destroy micro-organisms. Their effectiveness is often reduced by heavy soiling and it is preferable to clean then disinfect as a two stage process.
Bactericide	Literally, 'bacteria killer'. In practice, the same as disinfectant.
Best Before date	Date mark required on longer life foods that are NOT subject to microbiological spoilage. (For example canned or frozen foods). (Food Labelling Regulations 1996). This date mark relates to food quality rather than safety.
'Between pack' test	Sandwiching the temperature probe between two packs of food allows non destructive testing. Special flat probes are available.
Blast chiller	Equipment designed to cool food rapidly after cooking or heating. Usually employs a combination of cooled air and rapid air movement.
Bowser	Closed tank on wheels used to carry water.
Centre temperature	The temperature at the centre of a mass or piece of food.
Chilled display unit	Food display unit with facility to keep food at reduced temperature. Mechanical cooling may be transferred to food by direct contact (Dole-plate), by convected air movement, or fan blown cooled air. Some units use crushed ice. The efficiency of chilled display units is very variable.
Chiller/refrigerator/ fridge	Equipment to keep food cool. Normally between 0°C and 8°C.
Cleaning	The removal of food residues, dirt, grease and other undesirable debris.
Cold store/freezer	Equipment for keeping food at frozen temperatures. Usually set at around −18°C.

Compliance	Measures that satisfy the legal requirement
Compressor	Hot' end of the refrigeration plant where gas is compressed. (Later expansion of the gas in the 'evaporator' unit provides the cooling effect.)
Conduction	Transfer of heat (or cold) through a material, (normally a solid material).
Contamination	The introduction or occurrence in food of any microbial pathogens, chemicals, foreign material, spoilage agents, taints, unwanted or diseased matter, which may compromise its safety or wholesomeness.
Convection	Transfer of heat (or cold) through a liquid or gas by means of circulating currents caused by changes in density.
Cook chill	System of food preparation in which food is prepared in advance to be reheated several days later. Strict control of chilled storage temperature is needed if the food is to remain safe.
Cook freeze	System of food preparation in which food is prepared in advance and then deep frozen. If properly packaged the food may be kept for several months with no loss of quality.
Cooler unit	The cooling unit of a fridge system that passes air, often by a fan, over the cooling plate (evaporator) of the refrigeration system.
Coved	Rounded finish to the junctions between walls and floors, or between two walls to make cleaning easier.
Critical Points	Points at which hazards can be controlled. (See part 2)
Cross-contamination	The transfer of germs from contaminated (usually raw) foods to other foods. This may be: • by direct contact. They are stored next to each other. • by drip. One is stored above the other. • by food handlers who handle one then the other. • by equipment & work surfaces, used first for contaminated food.
Cryogenics	System of refrigeration using injection of liquefied gas into the storage chamber.
'Damped' sensor	Sensor designed to have a slower response to changes in air temperature. (A response time more typical of food.)
Defrost cycle	Periodic interruption of the cooling cycle to remove ice build up from the evaporator.
Defrost of equipment	Periodic switching-off of the refrigeration plant to allow ice build-up on the evaporator to thaw and run away. On most commercial equipment defrost is automatically programmed.
Destructive testing	Checking the temperature of food products in such a way that the food cannot be used. For example if the probe damages the integrity of packing.

Glossary	
Detergent/Soap	Materials for removing dirt during cleaning. Detergents and soaps differ in their composition but have similar action. They do not destroy micro-organisms (see disinfectant)
Disinfection	Reduction in levels of contamination on food equipment or in food premises, normally by the use of chemicals to kill micro-organisms. Disinfectants used must be suitable for use in food premises.
Domestic premises	Premises that are used primarily as a domestic dwelling. If the premises are used for commercial food preparation they will be subject to Food Safety Regulations. Specific requirements are given in Chapter 3 of Part 4.
Due Diligence	The legal defence, available in Section 21 of the Food Safety Act, that a person took all reasonable precautions and exercised all due diligence to avoid the commission of the offence.
EHO	Environmental Health Officer. Employed by the local authority to enforce Food Safety legislation. Can normally be contacted through the Town Hall or civic offices.
Electronic fly killers	Equipment to control flies and other flying insects. Insects are attracted by UV lamps and destroyed on a high voltage grid.
Eutectic plates	A plate that stores 'cold' in a panel of metal or plastic filled with a low freezing point mixture. Used to keep food cool when mechanical refrigeration is not available, e.g. in cool boxes.
Evaporator	The cold part of the refrigeration system where heat is removed from the refrigerated space.
Fermentation	Traditional process involving the growth of beneficial micro-organisms in foods. Important in yoghurt, cheese, salami, sauerkraut, bread, wine, beer and many other foods.
Fly screen	Fine mesh screen fitted to windows and other openings to stop the entry of flies and other insects.
Food	The definition of food includes drink and ice.
Food borne Infection	One type of 'food poisoning'. Invasion of the body by pathogenic micro-organisms transmitted by food.
Food handler	Anyone in a food business who handles food. (Part 3 gives a more complete definition for the training requirement).
Food Intolerance	A specific adverse reaction by an individual to a food or a component of a food which the majority of people would find wholesome. A number of different mechanisms may apply. Some may be genetic and inherited, some may be allergic. Reactions can be severe. Examples include nut intolerance and the coeliac intolerance to wheat gluten.
Food Poisoning	Illness transmitted by food. Caused either by infection or intoxication. Symptoms commonly include diarrhoea or vomiting. But many other effects are possible.

Glossary	
Freezer/Cold store	Equipment for keeping food at frozen temperatures. Usually set at −18°C or colder.
Fridge/chiller/ refrigerator	Equipment to keep food cool. Normally between 0°C and 8°C.
Gastroenteritis	Illness of the digestive system. Typically diarrhoea and vomiting.
Germs	Popular term for micro-organisms especially those that cause illness.
Growth	Bacteria, yeasts and moulds can grow in some foods depending upon physical factors such as moisture, temperature and so on. Growth may allow small initial contamination to reach levels which make the food unsafe or unfit.
HACCP	Hazard Analysis, Critical Control Point. – a management tool that gives a structured approach to identification and control of hazards. 'Classic HACCP' involves an multi-disciplinary expert team.
Hazard	Anything that may cause harm to a person who eats the food (see Part 2)
Hazard analysis	Identifying hazards, the steps at which they could occur, and the introduction of measures to control them.
Hermetically sealed pack	Food sealed into a pack designed to protect it from further contamination. Packs may be cans, jars, plastic pouches, plastic and board cartons. Food may be pasteurised or sterilised after sealing in the pack. Or it may be sterilised beforehand and packed in a sterile environment. In many cases, the pack seal must remain intact to protect the food from deterioration.
High Risk Foods	Ready to eat foods. Foods that have already gone through most or all of their preparation steps. There will be a 'High Risk' if these are contaminated or allowed to deteriorate because there are no further preparation steps to control the hazard. Examples are cooked meat, pates, meat pies, prepared salads, soft cheeses and so on. Cook-chill dishes and even cook freeze dishes are normally regarded as 'High Risk' foods even if they may be served hot.
Hygiene	Measures to ensure the safety and wholesomeness of food.
In-house catering	Work place catering operated directly by the employer rather than a contractor
Intoxication	Effects of poisonous substances. Some toxins may be formed in food by the growth of bacteria.
Intrinsic (contamination)	Already present
Load line	Usually in an open unit, a line to indicate the maximum height to which food should be loaded.
Load space	The area of a temperature controlled storage or display unit into which the food is stored or loaded. (There may be other spaces in the unit where air circulates but which are not available for storage.)

Glossary	
Load test	A test to establish the relationship between air temperature and food temperature at different points in a storage or display unit.
Logger	Electronic data loggers may be used to memorise data from temperature sensors during a period of time. Data can be recovered and analysed through a PC. Loggers provide more flexibility than old style chart recorders.
Low acid/acidity	Pickling or fermentation will increase the acidity of food and act as a preservative. Levels of pH below about 4.5 will prevent the growth of pathogenic bacteria. Low acid foods will have less acid, and therefore a 'higher' pH.
Low risk foods	Raw food or ingredients that are still to be cleaned or processed. Contamination of these foods is a low risk because later processing should make it safe. But low risk foods may transfer contamination to ready to eat foods, and they should be kept apart. Low risk foods also include many ambient stable foods such as bread, biscuits, cakes (but not cream cakes which are 'high risk'), cereals, and so on.
Lux	A measure of light levels.
Measuring system	A temperature sensor linked to a read out. Read-outs may include dials, digital displays, loggers or recorders.
Medical questionnaire	Form to be completed by new staff giving details of their recent medical history and that of close household contacts. Contact with certain infectious diseases may be transmitted by food handlers through food that they prepare.
Micro-organisms	Any small living organisms especially bacteria, yeasts, moulds and viruses.
Non-destructive testing	Temperature measurement that does not render the food unsaleable. May include 'between pack' probes or measurement of air temperature that is related to food temperature by a load test.
Open Food	Unwrapped food that may be exposed to contamination.
Pasteurisation	Heat treatment to kill bacterial cells but not spores. The time & temperature of the treatment must be controlled. Most types of food poisoning bacteria do not form spores so pasteurisation will make food safer by killing the heat sensitive pathogens.
Pathogen	A micro-organism that may cause illness.
Personal cleanliness	Measures taken by food handlers to protect food from contamination.
Pest	Animal life unwelcome in food premises. Especially insects, birds, rats, mice and other rodents capable of contaminating food directly or indirectly.
pH	A measure of acidity. The scale runs from 1 (acid) to 14. pH 7 is neutral. Levels of pH below about 4.5 will normally prevent the growth of pathogenic bacteria.
Piping hot	Thoroughly heated. Probably 70°C or hotter.
Potable	(Usually related to water supply). Safe to drink and acceptable for use in food preparation.
Private water supply	Water from a private well or spring rather than from the public mains.

Probe	A hand held sensor fitted into a metal sheath and often with a plastic handle. The probe usually measures temperature at its tip.
Proofing (against pests)	Structure of premises, especially doors, windows and the entry point of service pipes, to prevent the entry of pests.
Refrigerator/fridge/ chiller	Equipment to keep food cool. Normally between 0°C and 8°C.
Salmonella	A type of bacterium that can cause infectious food poisoning.
Sanitiser	Same as disinfectant. A term more common in American usage. Combined detergent/sanitisers are often used in a single stage process.
Sensor	The temperature sensitive part of the measuring system.
Shelf stable	Foods which do not normally suffer microbiological spoilage at room temperature.
Sneeze screen	Screen, usually glass or another transparent material, fitted to some food display units. May play a small part in reducing airborne contamination of the food.
Soap/Detergent	Materials for removing dirt during cleaning. Detergents and soaps differ in their composition but have similar action. They do not destroy micro-organisms (see disinfectant)
Sous-vide	Prepared recipe dishes that have been sealed in a vacuum pack and then heat treated and cooled for chilled storage and distribution.
Spores	Cells formed by some bacteria and many moulds which are able to withstand adverse conditions including drying and heat. Some spores can withstand very severe heat treatment.
Sterilise	Treatment with heat or chemicals to kill all micro-organisms and viruses. Sterilisation will kill spores.
Thermal properties	The physical properties of a food that determine how much heat it will hold and how quickly it will transfer heat through its mass.
Thermal simulant	Damping of the response of a sensor in such a way that it mimics that of a particular food to changes in temperature.
Toxic/Toxin	Poisonous substance. May be contamination from external sources for example chemical spillage, or produced by growth of microorganisms.
UHT pack	Ultra Heat Treatment. A high temperature / short time pasteurisation process. Used commonly for dairy products.
Use By date	Date mark required on microbiologically perishable pre-packed foods. (Food Labelling Regulations 1996. It is an offence to sell food after the 'Use By' date.

Glossary

Viruses	Microscopic particles. Some are transmitted by food and may cause illness. Viruses cannot multiply or grow in food.
Waste disposal unit	Unit to grind solid food waste to a slurry that may be flushed away with waste water into the drain.
Waste storage bins	Bins or containers used to store waste outside food preparation rooms whilst awaiting removal from the premises.
Waste transfer bins	Bins or sacks used for temporary collection of waste in food preparation rooms.
Water activity	See aW
Water filter	Filter, usually carbon, to remove possible chemical taints from water. Frequently fitted to vending machines.
Water softener	Unit to remove 'hard' elements from water to prevent scale build up in water heating equipment.
Wholesome	Food fit to eat.
Yeasts & moulds	Microscopic organisms. Some are desirable in food and are important to its characteristics, for example bread fermentation and the ripening of cheese. Others may spoil food and a few may cause illness.